'I walk my own path.'

Like a panther, she thought. A proud creature with little need for the company of others— or no, an eagle rather, flying high above the crowd. But why was he seeking her out? Had he marked her out as his prey?

Never. By birth she was a lioness, born under the sign of Leo and proud of it, even if she didn't really set much store by astrology. She'd never willingly become prey for anyone.

WE HOPE you're enjoying our new addition to our Contemporary Romance series—stories which take a light-hearted look at the Zodiac and show that love can be written in the stars!

Every month you can get to know a different combination of star-crossed lovers, with one story that follows the fortunes of a hero or a heroine when they embark on the romance of a lifetime with somebody born under another sign of the Zodiac. This month features a sizzling love-affair between **SCORPIO** and **LEO**.

To find out more fascinating facts about this month's featured star sign, turn to the back pages of this book. . .

ABOUT THIS MONTH'S AUTHOR

Geminis are famed for their love of variety and hatred of boredom—well, that's definitely true for **Rachel Elliot**. Her life is a pretty full one—divided between working as a television journalist, running a pony-trekking centre, and of course writing for Mills & Boon! All full-time jobs in themselves. As for romance—well, her fantasy figure hasn't yet appeared, but if anyone knows of a gorgeous Southern Irish vet, she reckons he'd fit the bill very nicely.

LOVER'S CHARADE

BY

RACHEL ELLIOT

MILLS & BOON LIMITED
ETON HOUSE   18–24 PARADISE ROAD
RICHMOND   SURREY   TW9 1SR

*First published in Great Britain 1992
by Mills & Boon Limited*

© Rachel Elliot 1992

*Australian copyright 1992
Philippine copyright 1992
This edition 1992*

ISBN 0 263 77766 9

*Set in 10 on 12 pt Linotron Times
01-9210-53168 Z*

*Typeset in Great Britain by Centracet, Cambridge
Made and printed in Great Britain*

CHAPTER ONE

'HE'S here again!'

Rory cursed softly as the sudden voice made her jump, sending the carefully poised mascara brush skittering over her cheek.

'Now look what you made me do!' She reached for a cotton wool bud, grimacing into the mirror at the reflection of the young woman standing behind her.

'Sorry.' The newcomer's grin showed a total lack of remorse. 'But he's here!'

'Who's here?' Rory leaned closer to the mirror, carefully wiping the black streak from her skin.

'You know very well who!' The young woman all but danced on the spot in her impatience.

'Candy, there must be three hundred people in the club tonight—would you care to give me just the faintest inkling who you're talking about?'

'Lucifer, of course!'

'Lucifer?' Rory resolutely schooled her features to remain impassive, but couldn't quite mask the glint in her tawny, almond-shaped eyes. Candy gave a delighted shout of laughter.

'You know perfectly well who I'm talking about. That's what the girls in the bar call him—tall, dark, ruthless as a pirate, handsome as Lucifer, and indubitably twice as wicked.'

Rory tilted her head to one side, pretending to consider, then shook her head.

'Can't say the description rings any bells.'

'Liar! The man who's been here for the past three weekends, always at the same table, always alone and always gazing at you with those incredible dark eyes of his.' Candy shivered deliciously. 'He looks at you as though he could eat you!'

Rory gave an unladylike snort. 'Better men than he have broken their teeth trying.'

'Aha!' Candy pounced instantly on the giveaway. 'So you do know who I'm talking about!'

A tiny smile played around Rory's generous lips. 'OK,' she conceded, 'maybe I have spotted him a couple of times. So what? He's just a club regular—just a man.'

'Just a man!' Candy's cornflower-blue eyes widened incredulously at the sacrilege. 'That's like saying the Mona Lisa's only a painting, or the Taj Mahal's only a building. He's—he's—well, I don't know for sure just what he is, but "just a man" he sure isn't!'

'Then what is he?' Rory began brushing her thick mane of rippling wheat-coloured hair over to one side, eyeing the other girl with mild interest.

'I wish I knew.' Candy's expression grew faintly wistful. 'We get every type of man in here—the medallion man, the oldest swingers in town, the boy racers just out of short pants, and the plain ordinary nice guys. He doesn't fit into any of those categories.' She sent Rory a curious look. 'Don't you wonder about him at all? Wouldn't you like to know more about the mystery man?'

Rory secured her hair with a heavily jewelled clasp and studied her reflection for a moment before giving a little nod. She'd do.

'Frankly, no. I've got better things to do with my time than speculate on men who look like pirates and have eyes like Lucifer. Like running a nightclub, for instance.' She sent Candy a mock stern look. 'And speaking of nightclubs, shouldn't you be tending bar somewhere?'

Candy clicked her heels and saluted smartly. 'Yes sir, boss, ma'am.'

'Then get going!'

Rory was smiling as the small, plump figure scuttled out of the dressing-room, but the smile quickly changed to a thoughtful frown. She was normally a very honest person—so why had she just lied through her teeth? Actually she was every bit as curious about the saturnine mystery man as Candy. She'd spotted him for the first time three weekends ago when she'd walked out on to the nightclub stage to perform her warm-up spot for the star turn of the evening. Her eyes had been drawn inexorably to the dark-haired, dark-suited figure, so still and silent among the laughing, chattering crowd. He had returned her stare and she'd sent him one of her brilliant, flashing smiles, but his features had remained completely impassive. Too much the professional to show that he'd rattled her composure, she had swung into her act with its usual brand of light-hearted, playful sexiness, switching from vibrant show songs to sweet, soul-stilling ballads with perfect ease, knowing she had the audience in the palm of her hand. Except for one member.

Try as she might, she couldn't stop her eyes from straying back in his direction time and time again, and every time they had it was to see that same unfathomable look on his face. He'd applauded politely at the end of every number, but seemed totally unmoved, and somehow that had made her try all the harder, as though it were imperative that she reach him. When she left the stage that night, the usual tumultuous applause was ringing in her ears, yet she felt peculiarly dissatisfied, as though she'd failed in some important task.

Following her normal routine, she had changed out of her show glitter back into a long and relatively modest black evening dress before slipping back into the main section of the club. To her annoyance she found herself glancing over in the direction of his table, but saw only an empty chair. She had been caught between relief and disappointment in that moment, but one of the waitresses had materialised at her side to ask a question, and for the rest of the evening she had been too busy to spare more than a passing occasional thought for the man with the still dark eyes.

He'd been back again the following weekend, and he had had just the same unsettling effect on her. But again, he had disappeared after her act, leaving her none the wiser, but with her curiosity well and truly aroused. It was a feeling she really wasn't accustomed to, and frankly she wasn't sure how to handle it.

Well, tonight she'd do something about it, she pledged silently. Tonight she wouldn't give him the chance to do his disappearing act. She checked her appearance in the full-length mirror behind the door, critically eyeing the strapless, figure-hugging red dress, then gave a little nod, satisfied with what she saw.

At twenty-seven, Aurora Jennings Blake was a beautiful, even stunning woman. That was a fact she accepted without false modesty or pride. Nature had simply seen fit to bestow on her a tall, long-legged and generously curvaceous frame, topping it off with a face that could easily grace any magazine cover, with its high cheekbones, slanting tawny-coloured eyes and full provocative mouth. Her part of the bargain was to keep that body in good working order, not to abuse it or damage it, and so far she had managed to do that pretty well. No mean feat really, considering the kinds of temptations. . .

Her head lifted as the nightclub band swung into the intro to her act and a smile played over her lips. Showtime. It was a moment that never failed to give her a frisson of excitement, almost a sensual thrill. She took a deep breath, letting it out on a low, pleasurable chuckle as she headed for the stage.

Tonight's crowd was a good one—Rory knew it the second her fingers curled possessively round the microphone, the atmosphere reaching out to enfold her like a lover's embrace, and she revelled in it, her eyes glowing, her whole body tingling in response. But even as her low, husky voice rang out with the first notes of the song, her eyes were seeking out the stranger, unable to resist his strangely magnetic pull.

He was there, just as Candy had said, in his usual seat, his attention as always fixed on the singer. Who was he? Why did he sit there in that most sociable of settings, solitary and apparently with neither need nor wish for company? He could have taken his pick of the women in the club—Candy wasn't the only one to be bowled over by his dark compelling features.

Feeling somehow challenged, Rory sent him one of her teasing, provocative smiles, but at the same time experienced a strange surge of protectiveness. Candy would be no match for him—it was doubtful if many women would be. Would she? She shrugged the thought aside instantly. Her own susceptibilities weren't about to be put to the test.

'Good evening, everyone.' As the music died away

she sent a shimmering glance round the room, a glance designed to send every red-blooded man's pulse racing just that little bit faster. 'Nice to see you all here, ready for another evening of gentle wit and repartee.' She raised a questioning eyebrow at the answering ripple of laughter. 'You had something else in mind?' She wagged a playfully admonishing finger towards the audience. 'You know this place exists for. . .' she paused for a fraction of a second '. . .rest and relaxation. A chance to recharge those tired old batteries.' She smiled slowly, knowing full well she was doing a fair amount of recharging all on her own. There was no harm in it. She knew it, and they knew it too—even the women in the audience responded well to her brand of flirting, recognising it for what it was.

'Take me, for example.' Her eyes widened in pretended astonishment as the suggestion drew the inevitable male response. 'I've had a hard week.' She lifted the microphone free of its stand and walked across the stage with the grace of a lazy cat. 'Know what I've been doing?' Her eyes swept over the audience as far as she could see beyond the footlights. 'Stripping.' This time masculine appreciation came at her like a wave and her answering smile was enough to light the room on its own. 'Hey, guys,' she raised her voice just a fraction above the hubbub, 'if any of you out there would like to help, I'd be delighted. I've still got another three rooms to do—that's a whole lot of wallpaper and paint to strip!'

As laughter rang out in the room, she nodded towards the band-leader and swung into her next song, a loud gutsy number far removed from the bittersweet love song she'd opened the set with. Well into her stride now, she glanced over towards the mystery man, wondering if that expressionless façade had finally dissolved into a smile. Surely he couldn't remain unmoved in the atmosphere she'd so skilfully created? Wrong. One glance was all it took to realise this was one hard nut to crack—his features still completely impassive. Even his body language told her nothing, or else it was simply a message she couldn't decipher.

Unconsciously she frowned slightly, determination building up within her like a tangible force. She'd get to him if it was the last thing she did. He couldn't remain immune for ever. For the remainder of her half-hour set, the audience was treated to vintage Aurora Blake—in fact, it was doubtful that she'd ever put on a more powerful show in any of the venues she'd performed in all over the world. She was consumed with it—driven by some mysterious need to conquer, to lay claim to one more devoted subject in this kingdom that was all her own.

But at the end of it all she left the stage to applause loud enough to rock the rafters, knowing with an angry certainty that she'd failed. She hadn't managed even to soften him, let alone subjugate him, and that rankled unbearably.

Instead of returning to the dressing-room to change as she normally did, she made her way through the backstage area back into the club, determined that he shouldn't simply disappear without trace as he'd done on the previous evenings. If he was already on his way out, she would simply have to find some way of stopping him, though right at this moment she didn't have a clue just what that would be.

Tonight, however, he was still at his table when she reappeared, and that threw her still farther off balance.

Damn the man—couldn't he be predictable in anything?

'Rory! You were incredible tonight. I've never heard you better.'

She had hardly taken a couple of steps before she was surrounded by clubgoers, and was forced to swallow a quick rush of impatience, summoning up her brightest smile as she accepted their compliments.

'Thank you. I'm glad you enjoyed the show.'

'You should be the star turn, Rory—there's not another singer to hold a candle to you.'

Obliged to give her full attention to the crowd around her, Rory felt a stab of annoyance dagger-sharp when she finally managed to glance over towards the mystery man's table, only to discover his seat was empty. He'd eluded her again!

'I have a drink waiting for you at my table, Aurora.'

She wasn't sure which had shocked her more—the quietly authoritative voice a couple of inches above her left ear, or the incredible tingle sent shooting through her skin by cool fingers laid on her bare shoulder. Taken aback, she could only stare in wide-eyed silence at the man who had materialised out of nowhere at her side. It was a surprise, too, to discover just how big he was. She was tall for a woman, but he topped her by several inches, forcing her to look up at him. It was a sensation she wasn't accustomed to.

'I'm sure you'll excuse Miss Blake,' he said gravely to the flock of fans still clustered about her. 'She needs to relax after that. . .' he paused infinitesimally, 'that amazing performance.'

His words might have been ambiguous, but the hackles rose on Rory's neck as if he'd been blatantly insulting.

'I take it you didn't enjoy my "amazing performance", then,' she said acidly, attempting to twist away from the hands laid casually at her waist as he ushered her towards his table. She would gladly have refused to go with him altogether if she hadn't been so curious about the man.

'I don't believe I said that,' he returned mildly as they took their seats.

'I don't believe you needed to.'

The faintest hint of amusement glimmered in his obsidian eyes as he raised one jet-black eyebrow.

'Is it really such a terrible tragedy that one person out of so many has failed to fall under your spell?'

She opened her mouth to give him a blistering answer, then closed it abruptly. So this was what the mystery man was like—arrogant and insulting. Candy was welcome to him. Even if he did have the most compelling eyes she'd ever seen—and a body to make the gods jealous.

'Did you want me for something in particular?' It was out of character for her to show a customer anything less than friendliness, but she was at a loss with this one, completely thrown off balance, and it showed in her abrupt tone.

He shrugged his broad shoulders and her eyes were drawn irresistibly to his chest. He was such a strange combination, sitting there so still and enigmatic, giving absolutely nothing away, yet managing to exude a raw and infinitely disturbing male power that seemed to threaten the female in her. And she had thought she could subjugate him! The very notion, now that she was sitting just a matter of inches away from him, was ludicrous.

'I wanted to meet you, Miss Blake.' His words were

simple, perfectly reasonable, yet strangely laden with threat.

'You have the advantage of me,' striving now to get the situation back under control, she spoke in her frostiest voice. 'You at least know my name—though I prefer to be called Rory.'

He gave a slight nod. 'So I understand.' He held out his right hand across the table. 'Adam Burns.'

Aware of a faint feeling of reluctance, Rory took his hand, half expecting her fingers to be crushed in a vicelike grip. Instead his handshake was firm but controlled—like everything else about him, she thought with a sudden rush of insight. His name too, with all its starkness and its distinctly masculine aura, fitted him exactly—though this man possessed none of the innocence and wonder the first Adam must have had in his Garden of Eden. His eyes, dark as bottomless pools, were hard to read, but held more than a trace of cynicism. Gazing into those dark eyes now, she was surprised to feel a faint stirring of recognition. But that was ridiculous—she was positive she'd never met him before.

'You wanted to meet me, Mr Burns,' she finally managed to rescue her eyes from the drowning pull of his and locate her voice. 'May I ask why?'

'Adam,' he corrected quietly. 'You're quite a celebrity in these parts.'

Foolishly she was disappointed, even though she should really have expected it all along. Heaven knew she'd been the subject of enough prurient curiosity in the few short weeks she'd been running the club. But he hadn't seemed the type somehow—she wouldn't have expected him to be drawn by the lure of so-called fame.

Her father had warned her it would be this way, his grey eyes unusually concerned as he sat with her in the club office.

'I thought you wanted to be out of the limelight for a while,' he'd said. 'You told me you wanted to get away from it all, to recharge your batteries after all the craziness. You won't manage that in the nightclub—they'll be flocking from miles around to see you.'

'And they'll stay because they like the place,' she had answered lightly. 'You never know, it could do business a power of good.'

He had waved the suggestion away dismissively. 'My club doesn't need gimmicks. It's already the most successful in the whole north of England.'

He hadn't meant to be hurtful, she knew that perfectly well. It was just his usual brusque, impetuous way of speaking. She should have learned long ago not to take him seriously. Unfortunately, she had never managed to develop a hide quite tough enough for his barbs to bounce off, and it seemed she never would.

Still, she was determined to help him whether he wanted it or not. The doctors had told him he must take several months off from the exhausting business of running a supremely successful nightclub, for the sake of his health, and looking at him now she could see all too clearly the deeply etched lines on his face, the distinct greyness of his skin.

'Perhaps I should sell the place and be done with it,' he said with an abruptness that showed he'd been considering the idea for some time.

'Sell it?' She gazed back at him in wide-eyed horror. 'But the club's been so important to you. You and Mum built it up from a seedy little run-down nothing! How could you even consider selling?' Then she paused, frowning. 'Don't you think you'll ever be well enough to run it again?'

He shot her a withering look. 'Don't be ridiculous, girl. I'm well enough now, it's those damn fool doctors who insist otherwise.' He paused, dropping his eyes to the desk. 'But I don't want to see my hard work wasted. Running this place is a heavy burden. I'm not sure you can cope.'

For a second she was caught between pleasure and pain. It was the first time in ages he'd demonstrated any kind of protectiveness towards her and she couldn't help warming to that. But to realise he had so little faith in her—that really hurt. She'd told him she wanted a break from her own very successful career— that had been bending the truth more than a little, but taking over the club, putting her own life on hold for a little while, had seemed a small price to pay for her father's health. Now it seemed he didn't believe she was up to the task.

'I can do it,' she said in a steady, even voice that belied the conflicting emotions churning within her. 'Just give me a chance and I'll prove it to you.'

He stared at her, almost as if seeing his daughter for the very first time, his eyes boring into her, and she suffered his scrutiny as best she could. Suddenly running the club successfully seemed to be the most important thing in her life. At last he nodded.

'A few months,' he said. 'But if it isn't working out, then I'll sell. And don't forget, even though I'll be thousands of miles away, I'll be keeping tabs on you.'

For the most part it had been easier than she had expected. Already to most of the regular customers she wasn't the famous Aurora Blake, but simply, Rory, and she liked it that way. But now it seemed this Adam

Burns was determined to dredge up her other life all over again. Shame—he didn't seem the type to go star-spotting.

'Ah,' she said softly, unconsciously toying with a beer-mat on the table. 'What are you, then, Adam? A rock journalist looking for a scoop? I wouldn't bother—they've all been done.'

'Why are you here? Running your father's club?'

Because my father's ill. The words echoed unspoken in her brain, sending tiny darts of pain through her veins. She was here, in her father's empire, because he for once in his life had been forced to accept that he was just as weak and vulnerable as any other human being. But she wasn't about to tell Adam Burns that. It was all she could do to admit it to herself.

She gave a tiny, indifferent shrug.

'My father wanted to check out a few interesting investments abroad, and I fancied a change of scene,' she said with forced nonchalance.

His dark eyes narrowed. 'Just like that? You were able to drop all your own commitments at the drop of a hat?'

She couldn't prevent a tiny ironic smile from curving her lips. Her agent had all but ordered her in front of a firing squad when she had broken the news to him— it was fortunate that she had already pencilled a six-month-long break into her diary, intending to spend the time writing new material. Only the promise of another potential platinum record had finally pacified him.

'Just like that,' she said at last.

He regarded her consideringly. 'Even though you've never done anything like this before? Wasn't it a rather weighty responsibility to shoulder?'

She was hard pressed not to glower at him—for a second there, he'd sounded just like her father, and she was getting tired of being put under the interrogation spotlight like this. Why did people—males in particular—assume that just because she was young, blonde and female, she couldn't handle pressure? Hadn't she proved her capabilities already in her own astutely handled career? But much as she'd have liked to resist his questioning, the innate honesty in her make-up finally compelled her to answer.

'I grew up in hotels,' she told him. 'My parents managed them—they were a very successful partnership for many years. I helped out, of course, and along the way I absorbed a fair amount of management skills.'

'You said your parents "were" a successful team,' he said. 'What happened?'

Rory flinched, the unexpected follow-up question hitting a nerve that was still raw even several years on.

'My mother died,' she said softly, then looked away, knowing her eyes were blurring with tears. It had been such a traumatic, agonising time, even now she couldn't talk about it without feeling pain. Her father had changed greatly with his wife's death, too. Before it he had been a loud, jovial man, given to spontaneous bursts of affection. After it he'd become withdrawn and moody, his formerly friendly nature turning acerbic and harsh.

It was a change Rory regretted bitterly. It had almost amounted to losing two parents instead of one. Just at the time when they should have been giving most to each other, he had turned away from her, and in its way that had been almost as painful as the loss of her mother. Now they managed to get along together reasonably well, but she knew their relationship was a million miles from what it had once been, and it was an enduring sadness in her life.

Adam Burns sat back in his chair regarding her steadily. She was both relieved and angered to see no trace of sympathy in his expression. She certainly didn't want his sympathy; in all probability she couldn't even have coped with it—but still, it would have been reassuring to detect some trace of humanity in the man.

'Something you don't like to talk about?'

She shook her head. 'It's not that, not really. I just don't like to dwell on the past.'

'And yet you still carry around the baggage of the past,' he said cryptically.

'I beg your pardon?'

He swept out one hand, indicating the club. 'This place—your performances. You haven't really distanced yourself from your old life at all.'

A faint smile touched her lips. 'I don't recall giving any indication that I wanted to.'

'Wasn't it difficult to step back from all that glorious limelight, then?' There was more than a trace of cynicism in his voice, but she was saved from having to answer by the arrival on stage of the star turn of the night. Mightily relieved, she gave Adam what she hoped would pass for an apologetic smile.

'I'm sorry,' she said, 'but I prefer not to chat while someone's singing. I know for myself just how irritating that can be.'

The knowing look in his eyes let her know she hadn't fooled him for an instant, but he gave a single nod.

'Another time, perhaps.'

'Perhaps.'

She turned to focus her attention on the up-and-

coming young band now swinging into their first
number. The club was just the right kind of venue for
them to cut their professional teeth on, and she was
glad to give them the opportunity. She'd even felt the
odd pang of nostalgia for the old days when she'd been
a young wet-behind-the-ears singer, just beginning to
make her way up the ladder. In some ways those had
been the best days, if she was honest with herself.

She glanced back at the man sitting across the table.
Why was he so interested in Aurora Blake? Was it
simply curiosity—or did it go deeper than that, and
was she right to have this strange feeling of apprehen-
sion? She gave a tiny shrug. She had nothing to fear. If
he was a journalist intent on digging up some ancient
dirt, he'd come up empty-handed. Even though she
moved freely in a world that had its dark and sordid
side, she had stayed clean, too innately fastidious to be
even faintly tempted.

'Are you a journalist?' she queried abruptly, forced
to raise her voice above the noise of the music.

Her eyed her mildly. 'I thought you didn't want to
talk while the band was playing.'

She made a wry face. 'At that decibel level, I don't
think it's going to matter much!'

He smiled, and her heart gave a strange little twist.
Lord, but this man was dangerous! A smile like that
could bring a lesser woman to her knees. Frankly, it
was as well for her that she was sitting down, because
she wasn't at all confident her own knees could cope.

'Would it matter to you if I were a journalist?'
Apparently finding it beneath his dignity to shout, he
leaned closer to her, and his warm breath shivered over
her skin. It took a major effort on her part not to

narrow the gap between them still further, but she managed to stay immobile.

'I was simply curious, that's all.'

He sat back in his seat, his knowing eyes never leaving her, and she took a deep breath, desperately trying to steady the sudden rush of adrenalin charging round her body. What in the name of all things wonderful was he doing to her? she wondered hazily. He hadn't even touched her, yet she was in severe danger of coming unglued before his very eyes.

If she had the sense she'd been born with she'd get up from the table right now, wish him a polite good evening, and scuttle back to the safety of the dressing-room, there to make a pledge never to risk being in his company again. But it would be impolite to leave in the middle of the band's set. More to the point, the urgent message rushing from her brain to her feet seemed to have encountered an impassable landslide en route.

Dammit, how much longer was the band going to go on playing? They were only supposed to do a half-hour spot, coming back later to do another set. Rory tried to sneak a surreptitious glance at Adam's wristwatch— she wasn't wearing her own since it would have looked totally out of place with the slinky black number she was wearing—only to have her eyes riveted on his hands. They were beautiful hands, though totally masculine. Hands that could relish hard physical toil— hands a sculptor would covet as a model for the personification in stone of strength. Yet they looked capable of tenderness too—lucky the woman stroked and caressed by those long fingers.

She swallowed hard, dragging her eyes away as she belatedly realised where her wayward thoughts were taking her. If he possessed mind-reading powers, she was sunk without a trace.

The band finally reached the end of their last number and she all but leapt to her feet, switching on her brightest, falsest smile as she looked down at him.

'It's been very nice to meet you, Mr Burns—Adam,' she said, about to hold out her hand to shake his in farewell, but changing her mind midway. After the things she'd been thinking, his touch would probably make her burst into flames.

'We haven't finished our conversation.' His tone was perfectly reasonable, affable even, so why did she feel as though he'd just issued a command? Unaccustomed to being told what to do, Rory tilted her chin slightly, her tawny eyes narrowing.

'I do have other customers in the club tonight,' she reminded him starchily. 'I can't neglect them.'

His hand snaked out to grasp her wrist as she made to move away, and she gasped, taken completely by surprise.

'Mr Burns!'

'Dance with me, Aurora.'

This time there was no mistaking the command, but, short of trying out one of the manoeuvres she had been learning in a regular martial arts class, there wasn't much she could do about it. The thought of flipping him neatly on to his back on the floor was a highly tempting one—and she was quietly confident she could do it, even though he was built like a rugby player. But she'd never enjoyed scenes—and something told her she would live to regret it mightily if she attempted to make a fool of this man.

'Just one,' she said graciously, managing to make it sound as though she were doing him a big favour.

She should be safe enough, she reasoned as they moved towards the dance floor where the discotheque was playing. The DJ was spinning one of his favourite high-tempo, high-energy discs—a funky little number if there ever was one. There need be no body contact at all. But Adam Burns had different ideas. As they joined the other dancers, he caught her hand in his and whirled her round into his arms, smiling at the astonishment on her features.

'This is a fast dance!' she gasped.

He nodded. 'I'm aware of that.'

'Then what are you doing?'

'I'm taking you in my arms,' he returned with a calmness she could only envy from the bottom of her heart. Right now she'd have given the nightclub to anyone who could restore calm to a pulse which had gone completely haywire and a brain in danger of short-circuiting.

'But why? We're the only ones on the floor dancing this way!'

'I've never cared for being one of the crowd,' he said softly. 'I walk my own path.'

Like a solitary panther, she thought. A proud, powerful creature with little need for the company of others—or no, an eagle rather, flying high above the crowd. But why was he seeking her out? Had he marked her out as his prey?

Never. The very thought stiffened her body in his arms and she all but scowled at him. By birth she was a lioness, born under the ruling sign of Leo and proud of it, even if she didn't really set much store by astrology. She'd never willingly become prey for anyone.

'Why the frown?' He brought the hand still holding

hers to her mouth, his finger tracing the shape of her lips.

'Because people are watching us,' she returned coldly. 'I dislike being the centre of attention.'

'Liar,' he said with soft mockery. 'You revel in it, Aurora Blake. It's what you were born for—to make men's heads turn and women's eyes grow green with envy for all that you have that they can never hope to achieve.'

His hand slid down over her back, his fingers splaying out over the firm swell of her bottom, pulling her body closer still to his. Her eyes widened involuntarily as she felt the virile power of him against her, but his expression remained unchanged.

'It's an awesome power, Aurora,' he murmured. 'But how do you wield it? With wisdom and restraint— or with reckless heedlessness?'

'I haven't the faintest idea what you're talking about.' She tried to speak steadily, but even to her own ears her voice sounded breathless.

One jet-black eyebrow quirked disbelievingly. 'I think you do, Aurora Blake, I think you do. And if I'm right in my guess that it's the latter—that you rule your nightclub kingdom with scant regard for the welfare and well-being of the poor fools who worship at your altar, then beware. You may believe you're inviolate, beyond the reach of lesser mortals, but you're wrong.' His night-dark eyes hardened to cold jet. 'Watch your back, Aurora, because I'm going to be behind you when you least expect it. And when you finally trip, I'll be there to make sure you complete your fall.'

She shuddered, completely at a loss to know what he meant, yet held helpless prisoner by the dark thrall of his warning.

'I don't. . .' she began.

'Take this as a promise of my intention,' he went on as if she hadn't spoken, and before she had time to realise what he intended to do, his mouth was on hers, harsh and demanding. She tried to squirm away, but his hold was secure, his strength far greater than hers. And even though his kiss was far from a lover's caress, she felt her body respond, acting as though it had broken free from the control of her mind, curving into him, begging for more of his savage domination.

It was only by an act of supreme will that she was finally able to wrench her mouth from his to look up at him with angry, blazing eyes. No longer caring that people were watching, she dashed one hand over her lips, trying in vain to obliterate the brand-mark seared there by his touch.

'How dare you?' she spat furiously.

His features showed no expression other than a mild amusement that only served to infuriate her all the more.

'There's no need to overreact,' he said in a soft voice that sent shivers along her spine. 'Judging by your "incredible performance" of earlier this evening, you're no stranger to men's kisses.'

'What the hell is that supposed to mean?' Bewilderment cut into her anger.

'Think about it.' He raised her hand to his mouth, pressing his lips against her nerveless flesh in a strangely mocking gesture. 'We'll talk again.' Before her astonished eyes he turned on his heel and walked from the discotheque floor, leaving her alone in the midst of the dancers.

'Not if I have anything to do with it,' she muttered savagely. 'Mr Adam Burns, you're in for a very long wait!'

CHAPTER TWO

'So COME on, what happened last night? How did the mystery man get you so mad?'

Rory groaned loudly and opened one eye to glare at Candy.

'Can't you give it a rest? It's a glorious, peaceful summer day—why can't you just lie back like me and soak up some of those gorgeous golden rays?'

'Because I'm a flibbertigibbet Gemini, unable to settle to any one thing for longer than two minutes at a time,' Candy returned comfortably, 'whereas you, my darling Rory, are a luxury-loving Leo.'

'You know I don't believe in all that.' Rory stretched her arms up over her head, revelling in the warmth beating down on her near-naked limbs.

'Then you should. Just look at us—if we don't prove astrology's got a lot going for it, then nothing does.'

'What do you mean?' Curious despite herself, Rory opened both tawny eyes to stare quizzically at her friend.

Candy grinned. 'Well, I'm supposed to be eternally childlike and curious. . .'

'True.'

'Exactly,' Candy continued, unperturbed by the wry interruption, 'whereas you are a hedonistic pussycat. Not all the time, of course,' she added hastily, seeing the frown crease Rory's smooth forehead. 'I know you're a demon worker too—but just look at you right now, all golden-limbed and relaxed in the sun. If someone were to stroke you, you'd probably purr!'

Rory's rich, husky chuckle echoed round the garden. 'That all depends on who the somebody was.'

'Which brings us neatly back to last night.' Candy sat back on her heels with great satisfaction, an expectant look on her small, pert features. 'Hey, I wonder what he is?'

'What he is is a rude and arrogant bully,' Rory shot back, irritated anew by Candy's persistence in probing for details about Adam Burns. She'd been at it for the past half-hour, ever since she'd arrived to interrupt Rory's precious sunbathing break. Heaven knew, with an entire house to decorate, there wasn't much time for sun-worshipping, but she'd never been able to resist the lure of the warmth for long.

'Is he indeed?' Candy thoughtfully tapped a fingernail against her front teeth. 'Then he could be a Leo too, I suppose.' She shook her head. 'No. That man hunts alone, never in a pack.' She screwed up her cornflower blue eyes in concentration. 'Taurus, possibly? No—he didn't strike me as the protective sort.' Her face brightened. 'Got it! I'll bet you anything he's a Scorpio.'

'Really?' Even though she tried to pack the single word with a wealth of bored indifference, Rory couldn't help but be curious. 'Which means what?'

Candy made a grimace and pretended to wince. 'Which means be very careful you don't get fatally stung, my darling Lioness.'

'Hah! He can try.'

'I'm serious! Scorpios can be real swine.'

'Aren't you getting your wildlife a little mixed up

here?' Rory put in mildly, though in truth she was more than a little disturbed by what she was hearing.

'Don't joke about it,' Candy returned solemnly. Then her eyes twinkled with irrepressible mischief. 'Mind you, if he is a Scorpio, then I'm even more envious of you. They're far and away the most passionate sign in the Zodiac.'

'So why should that make you envious of me?'

The blue eyes regarded her incredulously. 'Isn't it obvious? He's got you in his sights, girl.'

'So now he's a sharpshooter as well as a stinger?'

'You can mock as much as you like. It's perfectly true. I could see that predatory gleam in those dark eyes of his when he looked at you.' Candy gave a little shudder. 'Perhaps it's just as well it's not me in his line of fire. I don't think I could cope with all that smouldering passion—not to mention the possessiveness.' She gave a regretful little shrug. 'Wouldn't mind a little taster to see what I'm missing, though.'

'Candy!' Rory tried to look reproachful even through her laughter. 'I thought you had a king-sized crush on that singer we had at the club three weeks ago. You swore he was the love of your life.'

'So he was,' the other girl returned complacently. 'For two weeks.'

'Honestly, you're incorrigible!' Rory shook her head, sending her long wheat-coloured mane rippling about her cheeks.

'Can't help it. It's what I was born to be. Just as you were born to be queen of the pride.' Candy gave a philosophical little shrug. 'You can't buck fate.'

Rory rolled her eyes heavenwards and settled back on the sun-lounger. Just a few more minutes of this blissful heat toasting her limbs, then she'd rouse herself and return to the house. She had been halfway through wallpapering one room when the pull of the sun had grown too strong to resist a second longer.

Unconsciously she gave a little sigh. After years of living out of suitcases in hotel rooms and tour coaches, finding the shabby old farmhouse deep in the country had seemed like heaven—the second she'd spotted it, she'd felt as though she had finally found home. Her father had told her in no uncertain terms that she'd lost her mind.

'You don't need a house,' he'd pointed out. 'Look at all the travelling you do. After I come back to take over the club again, you won't be in it for more than a week or two at a time.'

'Everybody needs a base,' she had returned lightly, refusing to let him dull the excitement she had felt ever since finding the farmhouse. 'I haven't really had a home since. . .'

She'd been about to say, since her mother died, but the frozen, shuttered look on his features silenced her words, and she sighed quietly. Even now he still wouldn't talk about it, still wouldn't share his grief— or allow Rory to share hers.

After buying the house she had spent hours just walking through it, seeing in her mind's eye just how it would all look eventually—but turning those dreams into reality was sheer hard graft, and she wasn't halfway through yet.

She could have hired a team of professionals to do the work, of course, but she'd wanted to be able to look round at the end of it all and know she'd done it. There had been times, especially after a long busy night at the club, when she had been severely tempted to just throw in the towel and thumb through the Yellow

Pages to find the nearest painter and decorator to
hand. But a quitter she wasn't—in that, at least, she
was her father's daughter.

'Enjoying the sun, Aurora?'

Since she had been drifting luxuriously into sleep, it
took a second for the voice to register, but when it did,
it acted like a bucket of ice-cold water flung over her
sun-warmed limbs, and she jack-knifed upright, her
eyes wide with shock.

'What on earth are you doing here?' she demanded.

Tall, cool as an autumn wind despite the heat of the
day, Adam Burns strolled casually into her garden,
looking as though he owned the place. At her side,
Candy's bright blue eyes darted from one to the other
as she watched the meeting with unabashed interest.

Adam's gaze swept boldly over her golden-brown
body in its minuscule bikini, and she glanced quickly
round, vainly seeking a towel or a robe, anything to
cover her near-nakedness. Finding nothing, she turned
back to glare at him. She had never been ashamed of
her body before—why should she let him make her
feel this way?

'Please don't mind me,' he said softly as though he'd
read her mind. 'I didn't mean to interrupt your sun-
worshipping.'

'I was simply taking a break, that's all.' She tossed
her hair back from her shoulders, annoyed that she'd
felt obliged to explain. What she chose to do in her
spare time was absolutely no business of his.

'A break?' He raised a querying eyebrow.

'From turning this old wreck into a palace fit for a
queen,' Candy put in helpfully, oblivious to the glare
Rory sent in her direction. 'And I'm just off to buy
more wallpaper paste for her.'

'I asked you to get that three days ago,' Rory said icily as Candy got to her feet. 'I gave up on you in the end and bought some myself.'

'Then you'll doubtless be needing some more,' the redhead returned heartlessly, ignoring the frantic eye signals Rory was sending, commanding her to stay. She turned to Adam with a friendly grin. 'You probably won't recognise me, Mr Burns,' she said. 'I'm. . .'

'Candice Anne Levine,' he finished for her. 'You've been with Aurora for several years as her Girl Friday, and now you work at the club as her assistant.'

Candy's mouth pursed in an appreciative silent whistle.

'What are you?' she queried. 'A psychic?'

His lips curved in the faintest of smiles. 'Just interested.'

'There's really no need for you to go,' Rory cut in with a slight trace of desperation. 'I was just about to make some iced tea.'

Candy's pert features wrinkled in a grimace of disgust. 'Can't abide the stuff.'

'You loved it last week—you drank gallons of it!'

'Well, that's a Gemini for you—changeable as the wind. You'll pick me up at the flat as usual on your way into town this evening, Rory?' Barely waiting for a reply, Candy all but ran off down the garden path, leaving Rory feeling more alone and more vulnerable than she ever had in her life. Standing on a stage in front of hundreds of people was child's play compared to this.

'You were about to make some iced tea,' Adam reminded her quietly, and she blinked, strangely surprised.

'Would you care for some?' She extended the invi-

tation with extreme reluctance, since she certainly
didn't want him to stay a second longer than was
strictly necessary. Still, at least this way she'd be able
to escape into the house to find a robe.

He nodded.

In one graceful, easy movement, Rory swung her
legs off the sun-lounger and stood up, horribly aware
of his dark eyes on her. There was nothing unpleasant
in his scrutiny, no hint of lechery or desire, yet she felt
deeply uncomfortable standing there before him, clad
in only a few minute scraps of cloth.

'Are you embarrassed, Aurora?' he drawled.

To her annoyance a warm blush was steadily creeping into her cheeks. 'Well, I. . .'

'Don't be,' he cut in softly. 'You look like Eve in the
Garden of Eden.'

'Adam, I. . .' The blush deepened furiously as she
belatedly realised the connection between the two
names.

That strangely enigmatic smile played about his lips
again.

'Don't worry,' he said, 'there's no snake. Not here,
anyway.'

For a second she could only gaze at him, completely
at a loss. What on earth did he mean by that? Then she
gave a tiny shrug. The man was more than just a
mystery, he was an intricate, mesmerising maze. She
could never hope to get to his well-guarded centre.
And she'd never want to, she reminded herself resolutely as she turned her back on him and walked
towards the house, acutely conscious of his eyes following her every step.

She managed to walk with a reasonable degree of
grace and dignity till she reached the back door, then

scuttled inside as though her very life depended on it, taking the back stairs two at a time as she rushed to the bedroom to find a robe.

He was sitting in the deckchair Candy had vacated by the time she returned, and for a second she thought he had fallen asleep, his head tilted back against the wooden spar of the chair, his eyes closed, their long black lashes casting shadows on his cheeks. She knelt to lay the tray on the grass, then, frankly curious, turned to study him in a way she could never have done had he been conscious.

Looking at him with cool objectivity like this, it was hard to see why he had had such a powerful and disturbing effect on her, she realised, aware once again of a strange inner certainty that she had seen him somewhere before, but unable to pin the memory down. He was a good-looking man with his jet-black hair and intimidating jawline, but she had encountered any number far more handsome, yet none had stirred her the way he could with a single glance from those incredible eyes. In build, too, he was a prize specimen, lithe and powerful as an athlete. He'd look fantastic in swimming trunks, with those long muscular legs and that broad expanse of chest.

Even as the intoxicating thought shimmered through her mind, he opened his eyes and she flinched, horribly aware that he'd caught her staring. It was her own fault—she should have realised he wasn't asleep. Even with his eyes closed he hadn't seemed relaxed.

'I brought your tea.' To her annoyance, embarrassment was evident in her voice. What on earth was happening to her? He was making her act like a gauche schoolgirl—Aurora Blake, who could hold thousands spellbound with the power of her voice, who could mix happily with kings and commoners—stammering apologetically because a man who had wandered unwanted and uninvited into her garden knew she'd been looking at him! It was ridiculous. She was going to have to pull herself together.

'Thank you.'

She gave a single, ungracious nod, relieved that he at least hadn't made any comment. But then he didn't need to, it was all in his eyes.

Thoroughly out of sorts now, she turned away to busy herself unnecessarily with the tray—anything to get away from those black, compelling depths. She was completely at a loss to know how to deal with this man—even more at a loss to know just why he was affecting her this way. Open, friendly and honest by nature herself, she was happiest with others who acted in the same way, but Adam Burns was a riddle she doubted she would ever find the answer to.

And yet there was a part of her which longed to get to the bottom of this complex man, an instinct perhaps which told her the quest would be a worthwhile one. With her back still turned to him, she grimaced wryly at her own fancifulness. At this rate she wasn't likely even to scrape the surface, and she might as well accept that.

'How did you find my home?' Her composure regained, she turned back to hand him the long tall glass of iced tea, managing with an effort not to flinch visibly when his fingers touched her. 'I'm not even in the phone book.'

He gave a barely perceptible shrug. 'It wasn't difficult.'

From one of the nightclub staff, probably, she decided, refusing to give him the satisfaction of probing further. Considering how easily he'd discovered Candy's identity and background, finding out her address had probably been a walkover.

'But why. . .' she began.

'Why am I here?'

She nodded.

He seemed to consider the question, his eyes narrowing thoughtfully.

'You intrigue me, Aurora.'

That jolted her. She hadn't suspected the curiosity she felt about him might be reciprocated.

'Because of who I am?'

He shook his head. 'I already know who you are,' he said with quiet authority. 'I'm more interested in learning what you are—behind the façade of the star.'

Rory gave a nervous little laugh. 'What you see is what you get.' It was the sort of jokingly glib comment she might have made on stage. His expression remained unchanged.

'Then you're simply a brash and brassy singer—nothing else.'

She gasped as if he'd struck her, astounded beyond belief by the cool cruelty of his words.

'Brash and brassy?' she echoed incredulously. 'How dare you!'

'I'm sorry,' he said without the faintest trace of compunction. 'Have I hit a raw nerve?'

'Certainly not! But I. . .'

'That's the image you project on stage,' he continued mildly as if she hadn't spoken. 'Surely you wouldn't attempt to deny that?'

'I most certainly would!' she shot back hotly. 'Yes, I flirt a little, that's all part of the act, and people know that.'

'Do they?' His eyes narrowed. 'Are you really so sure of that?'

'Of course I am! No one could possibly take it seriously.'

'You think not?' He nodded slowly. 'But what if they did, Aurora? What would you do if some man out there in the anonymous darkness of the audience fell under the spell you create so skilfully and believed you were singing those sensuous songs just for him?'

She shuddered. Was he talking about himself? Could she have triggered some unwanted response in this mysterious man, entirely by accident? For a second she felt a frisson of fear. She was here alone with him, miles from the nearest neighbours. Damn Candy—she should never have taken off like that, leaving her to her own uncertain devices.

Suddenly restless, she rose to her feet and walked a few steps away from him, resting her elbows on the garden gate as she looked far away into the empty distance.

'I'd try to reason with him,' she said at last, hating the faint betraying tremor in her own voice. 'I'd probably try to make him laugh—that generally helps to defuse an awkward situation.' Which would be fine if she could think of anything even remotely amusing to say, she thought wryly. Right now her mind was devoid of humour.

'And if that didn't work?'

If that didn't work she'd run like hell and scream like a banshee; but she wasn't about to tell him that, especially since those long legs of his looked as though they could overtake her in seconds.

She gave a nonchalant shrug. 'If necessary I'd defend myself.'

'You're confident you could do that?'

'Can,' she corrected him, striving now to make her own voice sound as even as his. Something about Adam Burns told her he had great powers of perception—she'd do her own case no good at all by letting him know how deeply unsettling she found his questions. 'Not "could"—can.'

'Against this?'

Hearing his voice just behind her shoulder, she whirled round, her heart beating so loudly in her ears she felt sure he must be able to hear it too. The night-dark eyes bored into her as he moved closer still, and she braced herself, wondering just how he'd make his attack. She could defend herself—that hadn't been an empty boast. He might have the advantage of size and strength, but thanks to the martial arts classes she'd taken as regularly as she could over the past few years, she had a few tricks of her own up her sleeve. Enough—in theory at least—to put him on his back.

But the attack, when it came, came from an entirely unexpected quarter, leaving her completely without defence, as in one easy move he thrust his long fingers into her mane of hair and pulled her to him, his mouth silencing the startled cry on her lips. Too late, she tried to marshal her senses, only to find they had scattered to the winds, driven by the sudden flood of desire pulsing through her body.

It was like nothing she had ever experienced before—she had always been aware she had the capacity for passion, but it was an element of her own make-up she had kept sternly suppressed, her mind refusing to give in to the demands of a young, healthy body. In the life she led it would have been all too easy to succumb to the myriad temptations on offer, but she had seen them for the shallow, worthless things they were, and valued her self-respect too highly to accept dross when she knew she must seek for gold.

Now, though, with this Lucifer's touch on her body, his lips hungry and demanding on her own, she lost her will to fight, lost sight of all the reasons that had kept her aloof and apart from the crowd. In his arms she was no longer a thinking, rational person, she was merely a being consumed by the flames of need.

His hands swept boldly over her body, pushing aside her flimsy robe to scorch her trembling skin with his touch, and she pressed closer still, aching for more of the devastating fire. She was dimly aware that he had undone the ribbon ties of her bikini top, and she arched up towards him, mutely begging for the touch of his mouth on her naked breasts.

Then he laughed harshly, and her eyes flew open in shock at the sound.

'So this is how you defend yourself?' His eyes raked mockingly over her dishevelled nakedness, and she shuddered, still caught up in the storm he had unleashed, but horrified, too, to realise what she'd just been doing.

'My God!' she murmured, touching her fingers to her lips as though she could still feel the imprint of his ravaging mouth. 'What did you do to me?'

'I?' Adam's mouth twisted scornfully. 'Nothing that many others haven't done before me.' His eyes narrowed. 'Or are you going to play the game of the poor wronged innocent, Miss Blake? After that brazen little display, I'd advise you not to bother.' His gaze dropped to her breasts and she shrivelled inside at the contempt in his tone. 'I'd also advise you to cover yourself.

Unless toplessness is going to be the next feature of your act.'

'Get out of here!' Goaded beyond reason, she all but spat the words at him. 'I didn't even invite you here, you simply barged in, and now you have the unmitigated gall to stand on my land and insult me. How dare you?'

His dark eyes glittered. 'You haven't even begun to discover how much I'll dare, Aurora. But you will. I promise you, you will.'

And for the second time since she'd first met him, he turned on his heel and left her, his blistering words still seeming to echo in the very air around her. Slowly Rory walked back to the house, the glorious day ruined. For the rest of the afternoon she simply sat in the front room of the old farmhouse, surrounded by paint pots and rolls of wallpaper, oblivious to the chaos as she went over everything that had happened in her mind.

What was he trying to do to her? What strange warped game was he trying to play? He seemed hellbent on hurting her, but why? She had never even met him until coming to the club. Or had she—again she experienced that persistent feeling niggling at the back of her mind that somewhere she'd seen him before. She shook her head impatiently. As a singer she met dozens, maybe even hundreds of people; it was inevitable she would forget some of them. But not him. Never him. Somehow she knew with an inner certainty that even if she had met Adam Burns only for the most fleeting of moments, those dark obsidian eyes would have burned themselves into her memory for ever.

With a despairing groan she rocked forward in the chair, hugging a cushion to her as she relived those moments in his arms. She'd been under a spell—she must have been. He had driven her half out of her mind with little more than a few heated kisses, and the humiliation of knowing just how much she'd wanted him burned into her. How could she have reacted like that to someone who clearly despised her? It was beyond all reason. But it would never happen again.

'If you so much as lay a single finger on me again, Adam Burns, you'll hit the deck so fast you won't know what's happened to you!' she swore softly, her tawny eyes gleaming as she gazed unseeing across the room. 'You managed to take me by surprise this time—but those tactics won't work again. I'll be ready for you next time. So beware!'

CHAPTER THREE

THAT night, as she waited for the band to strike up her opening music, Rory felt none of the usual tingle of anticipation which made the whole business of singing so pleasurable. She had gone through all the rigmarole of dressing and making up almost on automatic pilot, deriving none of the normal pleasure from the procedure. It was all his fault, she thought with uncharacteristic gloominess. With a few choice words Adam Burns had somehow managed to take all the fun away—he'd tarnished her act, cheapened it even, by describing her as brash and brassy. Not that she agreed with him—if he were to appear before her right now, she'd still defend what she did and the way she did it to the hilt. Nevertheless, his cruel words had sunk deep, hitting right at the very heart of her.

Wondering if other people held the same opinion as Adam, she had casually questioned Candy as they drove into town together.

'How would you describe my act, Candy?' She had striven to sound offhand, unwilling to let the other woman know just how important her answer was.

'Total knock-out.' Candy slid her a querying look. 'Why? You surely must know for yourself just how terrific you are on stage.'

Rory smiled, grateful for the compliment but still no closer to the truth.

'Thanks. But if you were describing my act to

someone who'd never seen it, what words would you use?'

Candy screwed up her eyes thoughtfully. 'I'd say you were a sultry, slinking lioness who could have any audience purring with sheer pleasure,' she said triumphantly after a moment's consideration.

Rory rolled her eyes heavenwards. 'Don't ever get a job as a copywriter, will you!' She drove in silence for a while, then tried again. 'Would you say I was. . .' she stumbled over the words, 'brash and brassy?'

'Certainly not!' Candy was clearly scandalised by the very suggestion, and Rory gave a wry little grin, touched by her friend's fierce loyalty. 'Certainly you're sexy, but "brash and brassy" makes you sound like some kind of cheap pub singer.' She shook her head adamantly. 'You're a million miles from that. Why do you ask?'

Rory shook her head dismissively. 'No particular reason.'

'Don't give me that! You didn't just pluck those adjectives out of thin air. Someone must have used them—but who?'

Knowing Candy would only continue to probe till she got the truth, Rory gave in gracefully.

'Adam Burns.'

'He said that!' Candy's blue eyes glittered wrathfully. 'When?'

'This afternoon. After you'd deserted me to my dubious fate.' With an effort Rory managed to keep her voice free of reproach.

'The swine! Well, I hope you sent him scurrying home with his tail between his legs.'

Since that hope was so far removed from the reality of what had actually happened, Rory felt a peculiar desire to giggle. Instead she merely nodded. 'Something like that.'

Candy's reaction had afforded her a certain degree of comfort at the time, but now as she sat in the dressing-room, she was aware of a strange hollowness deep in the pit of her stomach. It was a sensation she wasn't accustomed to, and for a moment she wondered about it. Was she sickening for something? She dismissed the thought instantly. She had always been as strong as the lioness Candy would insist on comparing her to. Then why had her hands become inexplicably clammy—and how could she account for the unsteadiness of her breathing?

She glanced at her own reflection in the mirror and the answer came with the suddenness of a hammer blow. She was nervous. She was displaying all the classic symptoms. There could be no other explanation.

'Well, now you know what it feels like, kiddo,' she told her reflection ruefully. For years she'd sympathised hugely with those performers who'd become stricken with nerves just before going on stage—she even knew one world-famous name who regularly had to rush back to the dressing-room from the wings to be ill. Inevitably he would then go out and give the audience the show of their lives, but those few minutes were clearly excruciating.

It had never happened to her—in fact, quite the contrary, she revelled in the build-up to her own entrance, loving the rush of adrenalin that came every time she heard her own music. Now, though, she was sitting in the dressing-room, not even sure if she could persuade her legs to stand up and carry her to the stage.

'This is all your fault, Adam Burns,' she said aloud. 'You've done this to me.'

He'd done it by making her question herself, she realised. For years she'd gone blithely on in her own way, enjoying the applause, proud that she could send audiences home happy, laughing and satisfied at the end of one of her shows. Never before had she been forced to analyse what she did.

'Rory!' The voice startled her out of her reverie and she turned to see Candy in the doorway, her pert features anxious.

'What is it?' she asked.

'The band's played your intro twice already! You should have been on stage two minutes ago. What on earth's the matter?'

The vaguely fluttering nerves suddenly crystallised themselves into a hard painful little knot in her stomach and she bent over with a groan.

'My God, what is it! Are you ill?' Candy hurried to her side, putting a comforting arm about her shoulder.

'Not ill.' Rory sent her a rueful sideways glance. 'Just terrified.'

'Terrified? You? Of what?'

'Of going on stage tonight.' Rory shook her head in bemusement. 'I'm suffering from stage fright.'

'Stage fright?' Candy's eyes showed her total confusion. 'But you've never suffered a single nervous moment in your life!'

'Well, I am now.'

For a long moment silence hung in the air between them, Candy obviously searching for a solution to a problem she had never encountered before.

'Shall I tell the band you're ill?' she suggested

helpfully at last. 'I could say you've had a sudden attack of food poisoning or something.'

Rory gave a weak little grin. 'I'm sure Chef would love that!' She took a deep breath, willing the nerves to calm themselves. 'I'll be all right. And anyway, you know the old saying. . .'

'The show must go on,' Candy nodded, but her expression was still concerned. 'Are you sure, Rory?'

'I'm sure. Go and signal to them that I'm on my way.'

Making her way to the wings, then waiting for her cue, was probably the hardest thing she had ever done in her life. But it was nothing compared to the strain of walking out on to that huge expanse of stage and facing the crowd. She could only see the first few rows beyond the footlights, but knowing they were there was enough. She didn't dare look down at Adam's usual table—seeing him might just finish her off completely. As it was, she had to draw on reserves of courage she hadn't even known she possessed just to get her through the opening number.

And she wasn't on form. She knew it with the first note she sang, she knew it as she walked jerkily across the stage in a parody of her usual smooth-flowing stride, she knew it as she was forced to search her mind for the next line of a song she knew by heart. The audience knew it too—it showed in the polite but faintly puzzled round of applause, far less enthusiastic than she normally received.

She had always found being on stage an incredible joy, but this was nothing less than a nightmare, every second seeming to stretch for an eternity, and her usual spontaneity had completely deserted her, leaving her painfully self-conscious, horribly aware of every word she uttered.

She was more than halfway through the set before she managed to screw up enough courage to glance down at Adam's table, and her heart turned to cold stone as she spotted him in his usual seat, his dark eyes staring at her with their disturbing lack of expression. But as she looked at him, a tiny spark of anger flared within her. How dared he do this to her—how dared he rob her of something that had always been her life's blood? She couldn't allow it—couldn't let herself succumb to his manipulation this way.

With a sudden surge of defiance she tossed back her head, sending her long wheat-coloured mane rippling over her shoulders, her eyes flashing challengingly as she pulled the microphone free of its stand.

'You all seem kind of quiet tonight,' she told the crowd. 'What's the matter? Had a rough week?' She smiled as a communal murmur rippled towards her. They were uncertain of her, she could feel it as surely as if they'd appointed a spokesman to stand up and tell her so. Well, not for much longer. 'Come on, guys! Lost your tongues? Speak to Rory!' It did the trick. She was back in the driving seat, back in control, and the relief of it washed over her like a warm, revitalising wave. Only she knew, as she ran off the stage a short while later, just how big a strain it had been.

Back in the dressing-room she slumped into a chair, spent with exhaustion, cradling her face in her hands as she propped her elbows on the table.

'That really was quite a show you put on tonight.'

In a strange way she wasn't even surprised. Somehow she'd known he'd seek her out, or else she was simply too tired to register any kind of emotion at his intrusion into her dressing-room.

'Couldn't you at least have knocked first?' she said mildly. 'I might have been getting changed.'

'In which case it's unlikely I would have seen any more than I did this afternoon in your garden.'

She'd probably have slapped another man's face for that, she realised wearily—either that or lobbed back a playfully witty rejoinder. Instead she simply stared back at him, unaware of the naked vulnerability in her tawny almond-shaped eyes.

'What do you want?' she asked.

'I wanted to make sure you were all right,' he returned.

'Why shouldn't I be?' Stung, she sat up straighter in her chair.

He shrugged. 'You seemed a little—distracted on stage tonight. Not your usual exuberant self.'

'Not my usual brash and brassy self, you mean?' she shot back bitterly, then bit her lip. The last thing she wanted was for him to know just how badly his words had affected her. 'I was just tired, that's all.'

'Tired?' He seemed to examine the word. 'It seemed more than that from where I was sitting.'

'Oh, really?' Normally Rory despised sarcasm, but right now she couldn't prevent it from creeping into her voice. 'And just how would you diagnose my condition, Dr Burns?'

His dark eyes regarded her steadily. 'Normally when you walk on to that stage, you fill it with your presence—you're larger than life, riding the crest of a wave. Tonight you seemed—deflated. Like a pricked balloon.'

'How kind of you to say so!'

'Why, Aurora?'

'Why?' Because you robbed me of something I've always loved, she wanted to scream back at him. But the words stayed blocked in her throat. Not for anything would she give him the satisfaction of knowing his opinion could have such a devastating effect on her.

'I told you,' she said, looking away from his probing eyes. 'I was tired. Running the club and working on the house gets a bit much sometimes.'

'Then why do either?'

She frowned. 'What do you mean?'

'I mean that you could probably spend the rest of your life doing nothing more taxing than the sunbathing you were so clearly enjoying today.'

'I need to work,' she returned simply. 'It's important to me.'

'For the money? Or the fame?'

'Neither,' she shot back, nettled. 'Look, Mr Burns, it so happens that I was blessed with a pretty good voice. It's my extreme good fortune that I can use that voice to earn a living. Had my talents lain in a completely different direction—say stonemasonry, or cooking, then I'd have been equally happy to make those my career. But, one way or another, I'd have worked.'

Amusement glittered in the depths of his eyes. 'I can't quite see you as a stonemason.'

'There's no need to laugh at me,' she returned stiffly. 'I merely picked that as an example.'

'I wonder why it is that you object to being laughed at by me, when you invite laughter in your stage show?'

'When people laugh at the things I say on stage, they're laughing with me, not at me,' she explained. 'There is a difference.'

'So you have to be in charge of directing their responses?'

Not liking the way that made her sound, she was about to object. Then her innate honesty forced her to realise he was probably speaking no more than the truth, and she gave a single reluctant nod. Damn this man and his ability to force her into probing her own psyche more deeply than she'd perhaps ever done before.

'I suppose I do,' she muttered ungraciously.

'In fact, you like to be in charge of everything you do,' Adam went on.

Her head tilted back, her eyes meeting the direct challenge in his full-on.

'What if I do? The world needs leaders as well as those who prefer to be led.'

He nodded. 'But how do you lead? Wisely—or with disregard for those who follow you?'

Once again Rory was forced to curb the automatic response which sprang to her lips. To her knowledge she had never led anyone into anything she couldn't handle herself, but as he had pointed out before, she couldn't always know what sort of reaction she was stirring in those who listened to her songs.

'Which sign of the Zodiac were you born under?' The question was out even before she was really aware of it forming in her mind, but if he was surprised by her sudden change of tack, he didn't show it.

'Why do you ask?'

She shrugged. 'Curiosity. It simply occurs to me that you know a great deal about me, whereas I know nothing about you other than your name.'

He smiled faintly. 'And you think knowing my birth sign will fill in the blanks?'

She shook her head impatiently. 'Of course not! Forget it—I don't even know why I asked. Horoscopes are Candy's latest passion, not mine.'

'Ah yes, Candy, the changeable Gemini,' he mused aloud. 'What does she think I am?'

'Scorpio.' Rory bit her lip, appalled at her own lack of forethought. Now he'd know she and Candy had been discussing him.

'Then she's very intuitive,' he returned. 'Or else she too is thorough in her research.'

'She hasn't done any research at all—not into you, at any rate.' Rory gripped her hands into fists, horribly aware she was beginning to protest too much. 'She simply likes to take a stab at guessing the sign of everyone she meets, that's all.'

'In this case she guessed correctly.' Adam studied her for a moment in silence. 'So now you know two things about me, Miss Aurora Blake. Is there anything else you'd care to know?'

Do you happen to have a spare seven hours or so? This time she was able to trap the playful retort before it made it from her mind to her mouth, managing to content herself with an indifferent lift of the shoulders. The truth was she'd never been more curious about anyone in her whole life, but there was no way she'd give him the satisfaction of knowing that.

'Not particularly,' she shrugged.

'Very well.' The gleam in his eyes made her uncomfortably certain he knew perfectly well what she'd just been thinking. 'Then I'll take my leave of you.'

'Wait,' she said as he turned towards the door. 'There is one thing I'd like to know.'

'Yes?'

'Why do you keep coming to the club, all alone, week after week, particularly since you don't even enjoy my singing?'

That engimatic smile hovered over his lips. 'As I believe I told you already—you intrigue me, Aurora.'

As an answer it told her nothing. He hadn't even had good manners enough to protest that he certainly did like her singing, as anyone else would surely have done, given such a direct challenge. As the door closed behind him, she picked up a wad of tissues and threw them after him, scowling darkly as they fluttered harmlessly to the floor. Given another two seconds she might well have flung something a lot harder and heavier at him, even though she'd never done anything as temperamental in her life. It was the unsettling effect he had on her, making her question everything she'd always taken for granted.

Not that that in itself was a bad thing, she acknowledged—but she bitterly resented the fact that he, Adam Burns, should have that kind of influence over her. An influence strong enough to rob her of the natural exuberant self-confidence that had always been a central, unthinking part of her personality. Even her father couldn't exert that kind of power over her. So why Adam? What was it about him that one look from those obsidian eyes could reduce her to mush?

Well, she'd simply have to find the strength within herself to resist that power, she decided grimly, rising to her feet and reaching for the long black dress she'd laid out earlier to change into. Right now she had enough on her plate with the club and the house—she simply didn't have time to contend with him too.

*   *   *

'I reckon I've got him sussed,' Candy announced triumphantly as they drove through the empty late-night streets towards Candy's flat.

'You've got him what?' echoed Rory.

'Sussed. You know, worked out, pinned down.'

'Are we talking about Adam Burns, by any remote chance?' Rory shot her an incredulous look. 'I'll give you a month's extra salary if you've managed to suss that one out.'

'Watch it! I'll hold you to that. So, do you want to know my theory about your mystery man?'

Rory grimaced irritably. 'He is most definitely not my mystery man,' she said, ramming the gear-stick emphatically home, then wincing apologetically. There was no need to take out her irritation on the car.

'Oh,' Candy nodded. 'Then you won't be particularly interested in what I've worked out, then.'

Rory shrugged. 'Not particularly. But since you're obviously bursting to tell someone, I don't mind listening.'

Candy shook her head. 'I wouldn't want to bore you with the details. Forget I mentioned it.'

'Fine.'

'Fine.'

Rory turned her attention to the road ahead, gripped by two almost equally powerful temptations—the first being to take her hands off the wheel and shake Candy by the shoulders for being so infuriating. That longing she managed with an effort to suppress—the other was made of sterner stuff, and at last she gave in to it.

'Come on, then,' she said impatiently.

'I beg your pardon?' Candy's expression radiated innocence.

'For the love of Mike! Tell me what you've worked out!'

Candy chuckled, completely unmoved by her outburst. 'Thought you wouldn't hold out much longer than five minutes,' she said with smug complacency. 'Actually it was more like a minute and a half.'

'Candice Anne Levine, if you entertain any real hopes of seeing your next birthday, I suggest you start talking. Now!'

'My, my, the lioness is grouchy tonight!' Candy returned mockingly. 'Has the scorpion been stinging you again?' She held up her hands in mock surrender as Rory sent her a black sidelong scowl. 'Ok, Ok, I won't tease you any more. As I believe I've told you already, the man's got his eyes heavily fixed on you.'

Rory groaned. 'We're not back on that track again, are we? As theories go, that's a dead duck.'

'Just because you say so doesn't make it so, however,' Candy returned complacently. 'And I reckon it's the truth. However, if you don't want to hear any more. . .'

'Candy!'

The other girl giggled at the threatening note in Rory's voice. 'You really are a lioness when you growl like that! Anyway, here's my theory. Scorpios are intensely possessive and jealous individuals, and whether you like it or not, your Adam Burns has decided to claim you for his own.'

'He can claim all he likes,' Rory shot back hotly. 'He certainly won't get me!'

'Try telling him that. Now stop interrupting! Because he's laid claim to you, he doesn't appreciate the fact that you're public property.'

'I am not!' snapped Rory.

'When you're on stage you are.' Candy refused to be
budged. 'But he wants you all to himself—and he's
found the best way to do that is to take away the
pleasure you find in singing. Pretty Machiavellian, huh?
It worked too—just look at the way you were on stage
tonight!'

A deep frown creased Rory's smooth brow. Much as
she hated to admit it, there was a certain crazy logic in
Candy's theory.

'Let's change the subject,' she said abruptly. 'I don't
want to talk about this any more.'

'Because you know I'm right, that's why,' Candy
said shrewdly. 'The only question is—what are you
going to do about it?'

'I don't really see that I have to "do" anything,' Rory
averred. 'It's his problem, not mine.'

'You're fooling no one with that line,' Candy scoffed.
'Not even yourself. Because the real problem, Rory,
my sweet, is that you're just as attracted to him as he
is to you.'

'Nonsense!'

'You are. Otherwise his crack about you being brash
and brassy would have slid right off your back. You've
had bad reviews before—show me a performer who
hasn't! But you've always managed to rise above them.
Till now.'

It was with a deep sense of relief that Rory reached
Candy's road and drew to a halt before the building
where she lived. Fond though she was of the other girl,
she couldn't take much more of this. Especially since
she was horribly afraid Candy might be right.

The thought played over and over in her mind as she
waved an absent-minded farewell and drove off into
the night alone. Ironically, Candy had reached her

conclusions on pretty scant evidence—she didn't even know about the heated moments in Adam's arms—if she knew how strongly Rory had responded to his touch, she'd be completely convinced.

'Oh, hell,' she muttered miserably to the empty car. 'Why him? Of all the men I've met since I even realised there was a difference between the sexes, why did it have to be this one who got under my skin?'

And, more to the point, how was she going to dislodge him?

CHAPTER FOUR

RORY stared at the figures on the page, a frown of deep concentration creasing her features. She had fast come to discover that the most difficult part of running the nightclub was the inevitable mountain of bookwork she had to contend with. Actually the bulk of it was being done in her father's absence by his accountant, but still there was enough left for Rory occasionally to feel swamped. Sheer determination to prove she could do the job her father hadn't believed her capable of kept her plugging away at it. Tonight she would far rather have been getting on with a hundred and one other things, but conscience had dictated that she must get the books finished first. And of course that also meant she couldn't possibly spare the time to do her usual singing spot in the club.

At the thought, her conscience gave another little twinge and she groaned aloud in the empty office.

'Ok,' she muttered irritably, 'so I'm a liar. The whole truth is I simply couldn't face another attack of those hellish nerves on stage. Are you satisfied now?'

'Speaking to yourself, Aurora?'

Rory jumped as though she'd been shot at the sound of the lazily amused voice materialising apparently out of nowhere. Her eyes lifted from the books before her on the desk to the tall, powerful figure standing just a few feet away. How long had he been there? Had he heard what she'd been saying? The very thought brought a flush that was half embarrassment, half anger to her cheeks.

'I didn't hear you knock on my door,' she said accusingly.

He gave a barely perceptible shrug. 'You were obviously too engrossed in your work to hear anything.'

She scowled darkly, realising he'd deftly avoided answering her implicit question. She opened her mouth to ask it again, more directly this time, then closed it with a snap. To belabour the point of whether or not he had knocked would only make her sound shrewish, and she didn't want that added to his list of uncomplimentary adjectives, along with brash and brassy!

'Did you want something, Mr Burns?' Try as she might to sound polite but distant, she couldn't help but hear the ice in her own normally warm voice, and that annoyed her. Why couldn't she treat him with the same cool indifference as he showed her?

'Why haven't you sung tonight?' he demanded.

She flinched, caught on the raw by the starkness of the question. Anyone else would have had tact enough to at least dress it up a little, she thought wryly. Not Adam Burns, though—oh no, he had to go straight for the jugular. But then she should have anticipated that, since Candy had already warned her of the Scorpio ability to be cruel.

She gestured towards the books lying open on the desk. 'Because of these,' she said simply. 'The bookwork has a tendency to pile up if I don't keep on top of it.'

The look in his eyes told her quite clearly he didn't believe a word of it, and she struggled to maintain a bland, ingenuous expression on her own features, wondering if even he could be cruel enough to brand her a liar.

After a long moment, a tiny smile began to play around his lips. 'How refreshing to meet someone so dedicated,' he said with only the very faintest trace of mockery. 'But how strange. I'd have thought the weekend would be your busiest time.'

'It is,' she agreed, then bit her lip, only seeing the trap he'd set for her when she'd already tumbled straight into it.

'Then surely it's rather a waste of time to bury yourself away on a Saturday night when you'll have the bulk of the work to contend with tomorrow—when the club's closed.'

Never being lost for words had always been one of Rory's great talents, but right now it seemed to have deserted her completely, and she was forced to look away from his dark, probing eyes, horribly aware of his apparent ability to see straight through her.

'If there's nothing else, Mr Burns, I really do have work to do,' she said at last, reaching for one of the ledgers.

'But there is something else.' Before her astonished eyes he calmly sat down in the chair at the opposite side of the desk.

'Well, since you ask so nicely, I suppose I can spare you a couple of moments,' she said, with a touch of her old wry humour.

'I think you'd better find rather more time that that,' he returned coolly. 'What I have to say is important.'

Knowing when she was beaten, Rory gave a heavy sigh and shut the ledger with a thud. 'Then you'd better say it,' she said, managing with an effort to affect a calmness she was far from feeling.

'I want to buy this club.'

It was as though he'd kicked her hard in the stomach. Profoundly shocked, she stared back at him, unable even to find words. So that was why he'd been in the club so often over the past few weeks—he'd been checking out the lie of the land, assessing the place as a possible investment. So much for Candy's theory that he'd been stalking Rory! This scorpion had had prey of an entirely different nature in his sights. For one terrible moment she felt a bubble of hysterical laughter bubbling up inside her.

'I hardly think it's a laughing matter,' he said sharply.

Rory shook her head. 'I wasn't laughing,' she said, all too horribly aware of a wave of disappointment washing over her. She wasn't disappointed at all, she told herself severely—it was just that her pride had taken a bit of a blow. Surely any woman would have reacted the same way on discovering a supposed admirer was in reality only after her possessions?

'Then what do you have to say about it?'

'What do I have to say?' She gazed back at him, her eyes wide and incredulous. 'No, Mr Burns, that's what I have to say. The club's not for sale.' And certainly not to you, she added under her breath.

One jet-black eyebrow raised lifted lazily. 'I have it on good authority that your father is seriously considering selling,' he said calmly.

'Then your "authority" isn't as good as you think,' she snapped, mentally crossing her fingers against the lie.

'You're confident your father would say the same thing?'

Try as she might she couldn't hold his gaze. His eyes were just too probing, too all-seeing.

'He may have considered the possibility of selling at some stage in the past,' she conceded reluctantly. 'But not any more.'

'Why not?'

'Because I'm running the place now.' Unconsciously she tilted her chin defiantly as she gazed back at him, as though daring him to challenge her authority.

His lips quirked. 'Having had no experience whatso-ever of club management.'

'Perhaps not, but, as I already told you, I grew up in the business,' she returned hotly.

'Which no doubt accounts for the ease you display in dealing with the public,' he said. 'But as to the actual work involved. . .' he shook his head, 'I don't think you can have any conception of that.'

By now she was having to work hard to keep her fast-rising temper in check. Just what did he think she was—a spoilt little rich kid who'd grown up being waited on hand and foot? It was an attitude she had encountered before admittedly—from people who assumed that because she had grown up in hotels, she had been able to enjoy all the comforts afforded to the customers. The reality had been considerably different.

'I take it then that you neither have children of your own, nor indeed a hotel,' she said now, with more than a slight trace of sarcasm. 'Because if you did, you'd know as well as I that any youngsters growing up in that sort of background learn from a relatively early age all the joys of hotel life—like being called upon to wash sinkloads of dishes when the dishwasher packs up—or to change dozens of beds when the chamber-maid calls in sick. Then of course there's waiting at table and serving behind the bar when you're old enough.' She gave a single decisive nod. 'I think I can claim to have worked my apprenticeship in the licensed trade. Can you say the same thing, Adam?'

There was a faint gleam in his dark eyes. 'I believe I can,' he said slowly. 'Though you're half right—I don't have any children. I do, however, own a hotel. Or, to be more precise, several of them. And a couple of nightclubs.'

Rory gazed at him in disbelief. Several hotels? A couple of nightclubs? Just who exactly was she dealing with here?

'Who are you, Adam?' she asked at last.

A faint smile curved his lips. 'You already know my name,' he said.

'But apparently not your identity.'

He shrugged. 'Perhaps you'll recognise my nickname.'

'Nickname?'

'Given to me by one of the Sunday newspapers which chose to run a feature on my business interests.' His mouth twisted wryly. 'As often happens with these things, the nickname stuck.'

'What is it?' Even as she spoke she was gripped by a niggling feeling of premonition.

His expression never altered as he looked at her. 'I'm known as the Midnight Raider.'

The penny dropped with a resounding clunk in her brain. The Midnight Raider. Of course! Now that he'd told her, she couldn't understand why she hadn't recognised him right from the start—she'd seen the article, had even marvelled at the way the photographer had managed to capture those dark, brooding eyes.

She looked into those eyes now and her heart sank. He deserved his nickname. Like a raider, he had swooped on a series of nightclubs, probably before their owners even had time to fully appreciate what had hit them. According to the journalist who had written the article, he was equally adept at raiding hearts. There had been a series of photographs showing Adam with a series of women, each one more gorgeous than the last, and each one looking up at him with undisguised adoration.

Ruthlessly quashing a ludicrous little niggle of jealousy, Rory frowned, wishing she had paid more attention to the text—she could recall its admiring tone, even if not the actual words. The reporter had clearly been knocked sideways by Adam's undeniable charisma, which doubtless meant he had been interviewed by a female, she thought disparagingly.

'So now you think you're going to add my club to your pirate's treasure trove,' she said bitterly.

'I'm known as a raider, not a pirate,' he reminded her calmly, though she could see a faint trace of anger in the barely perceptible tightening of his features.

'There's a difference?' she taunted.

'I believe so, yes.'

She waited expectantly, but he didn't elaborate. How typical of this unbelievably arrogant man, she thought angrily—anyone else would surely have felt compelled to defend themselves, or at least to explain, but not him. He seemed to think she should simply take him at his word. Well, she wasn't going to let him off the hook that easily.

'Go on,' she said tersely. 'I'm interested to hear how you define that difference. I don't imagine the dictionary would draw much of a distinction between the two trades.'

To her further annoyance she saw a faint trace of

amusement in his eyes. How dared he laugh at her! But before she could speak he held up one imperious hand, effectively commanding her silence.

'I didn't choose the epithet for myself,' he said pointedly. 'It was assigned to me by the press, a breed which in my experience cares little for such irrelevancies as accuracy.'

Score one for the opposing team, Rory thought wryly. After some of the descriptions she'd seen tagged on to her own name in newspaper reviews, she could hardly disagree. She nodded in reluctant concession.

'Very well, I'll give you that.'

'Thank you.' A wintry little smile played over his features, warming them not one iota. 'I take it then that you have also come in for your share of press flights of fancy?'

Even though she knew perfectly well in her heart of hearts that it was ridiculous, she couldn't help but feel faintly aggrieved. Had her share? At one stage in her career, it had seemed you couldn't open up a rock paper or one of the tabloids without seeing her tumbling golden mane and her lazy catlike smile captured by one of the many photographers who seemed to dog her every step. Everyone in the country must have seen them. Except him, apparently. There again, Adam Burns was hardly the type to read rock reviews or, for that matter, the tabloids. His morning reading would doubtless be the *Financial Times*.

'You could say that,' she returned wryly. 'But please, don't let me distract you from what you were saying. It was so terribly fascinating.' She flashed him her most sacharine-sweet and blatantly insincere smile, mentally notching up a point for herself when irritation tightened his lips. In this war of nerves, it was infinitely reassuring

to know she could at least get the occasional barb past
that glacial exterior.

'I prefer to let my reputation speak for itself,' he said
with a quiet authority she could only envy. 'I see no
need to explain my business actions.'

He didn't add the words 'to you', but they hung
unspoken in the air between them, and she scowled
angrily, stung by his condescension.

'If you entertain any serious notions of buying my
club, then I think you certainly do need to explain your
business actions,' she shot back hotly.

'But I don't.'

'What?' Rory flung her head back sharply, sending
her long mane tumbling in golden disarray. 'But you
just said. . .'

'I want to buy your father's club,' he said succinctly.
'Despite your obvious fondness for the place, you're
none the less nothing more than a temporary caretaker.
If I need to explain anything at all, it will be for his
benefit, not yours.'

In that instant she could happily have hit him.
Unconsciously she clenched her hands into fists, anger
sending a rare flush to her cheeks. In her early days as
a singer she had encountered those who had wrongly
assumed she was nothing more than a beautiful but
empty-headed blonde. It was a belief she had swiftly
dispelled. To have Adam Burns now treating her as
some kind of bimbo infuriated her beyond belief.

'My father left me in sole and total charge,' she said
slowly, battling to retain control of her emotions. 'In
his absence all decisions are taken by me and me
alone.'

'With his ultimate decision on whether or not to sell

entirely dependent on how successfully you cope in his absence.'

She gaped at him in blank astonishment, then frowned. 'Did Candy tell you that?'

His expression never wavered. 'It was an educated guess.' His eyes regarded her speculatively. 'Why should it matter to you so much whether he sells or not? You'll be returning to the glamorous world of rock as soon as he returns. Won't you?'

'Perhaps.' Rory bit her lip, appalled at her own lack of discretion. What on earth had made her let that slip? No one, not even Candy, knew that she was undecided about her future moves. The truth of the matter was that even before she had agreed to take over the club she had been plagued more and more by a feeling that she had done all she could do in the music business. After all, she had enjoyed ten very successful years, but the so-called glamour Adam had referred to had in many ways begun to pall. Living the life of a nomad, travelling from city to city, never being able to put down roots in any one place, had taken its toll.

She turned away, sending up a silent but not very optimistic prayer that her tiny slip had passed unnoticed. Until she'd made up her mind one way or the other, the last thing she needed was for rumours of an imminent retirement from music to start circulating.

'In answer to your question,' she went on firmly, 'it's important to me because this club means a great deal more to my father than you could possibly understand—maybe even more than he understands. He and my mother bought it when it was nothing—a run-down place with a shabby décor and an even shabbier reputation. But it was the first place they'd owned together, after years of managing hotels for other people.' She paused, her eyes growing faintly misty. 'It gave him a purpose in life after she died.'

'A crutch?'

She frowned, disliking the term. 'A purpose in life,' she repeated emphatically. 'There's a difference. He's a strong man, but he needed a direction.'

'And you think he still needs that?'

Unthinkingly she nodded, then mentally kicked herself. Damn, she was doing it again—revealing far too much of her innermost thoughts, and to this man of all people!

'Isn't it rather presumptuous of you to decide what he needs?' he asked curiously.

'Presumptuous?' The accusation took her aback. 'I care about him, that's all.'

'Naturally.' He nodded slowly. 'But you can't live his life for him. Or make his decisions.'

'How dare you?' Abruptly, unexpectedly the anger simmering inside her reached boiling point. 'You know next to nothing about me and you don't know my father at all, yet you have the nerve to say such things! If anyone's being presumptuous around here, it's you!'

'Outside observers can often see things more clearly, than those intimately involved,' he said calmly, apparently unmoved by her outburst.

'Particularly when those observers have their own ulterior motives in mind,' she shot back. 'Do you really believe I can't see through your little game, Adam Burns? You think you're going to convince me that selling the club would be in my father's best interests, with you as the kindly soul just waiting to take the burden off his hands. Well, it won't wash. I won't allow you to manipulate me in this way.'

'Even if it really is a burden to him?' The dark eyes
bored into her and she felt a shiver run along her spine.
When he looked at her that way he had the most
uncanny knack of making her believe he could see right
into her soul, and it was a deeply uncomfortable
sensation. 'Perhaps it's really you who are hanging on,
loath to lose that last link with your mother. Think
about it, Aurora—decide whether your desire to hang
on to the club really is for his sake—or yours.'

Unwillingly she watched as he got to his feet,
strangely unable to tear her eyes away, fascinated all
over again by the power of the man, the sheer pagan
strength contained beneath the civilised veneer of a
dark, elegant suit.

Suddenly one of her father's favourite old sayings
popped as if from nowhere into her mind. 'Keep your
friends close, but your enemies closer still,' she murmured quietly as the door closed softly behind him.
She'd never really understood the meaning behind the
adage—until now. But it was good advice, advice she
would do well to take. Now that he'd told her he
wanted the club, Adam would probably expect her to
keep him at a wary arm's length. It would be the
obvious thing to do under the circumstances. So she'd
do just the opposite, keeping him close and at the same
time keeping a watchful eye on all he was doing. The
only snag was—how close could you keep a scorpion—
without being fatally stung?

'Damn and blast the man!' Rory sat up in bed, scowling
fiercely into the darkness as though the object of her
condemnation was sitting right in front of her. Even
though she hadn't got to bed till the small hours, and
had been feeling totally exhausted, she'd been tossing

and turning for what seemed like hours, utterly unable
to sleep. It wasn't hard to work out the reason for her
totally uncharacteristic bout of insomnia, either—
Adam Burns.

'You turn up in my garden uninvited, you ruin my
act, you tell me you want to buy my club, now you're
destroying my sleep!' she groaned. 'Are you trying to
kill me off by degrees?' Giving up the battle to make
her restless mind switch off, she flung back the duvet
and got out of bed. By rights she should be sleeping
the sleep of the just by now, she realised despondently
as she switched on the bedside lamp—instead she'd
been reliving everything over and over in her mind. So
now on top of everything else she'd look a wreck in the
morning.

'Mr Burns, you have a great deal to answer for,' she
muttered savagely, hauling the insubstantial scrap of
ribbon and lace that claimed to be a nightdress over
her head and reaching instead for jeans and a sweatshirt. There seemed little point in trying to do battle
any longer against the inevitable. She simply wasn't
destined to get any rest, so she might as well do
something useful with the empty hours.

She padded barefoot down the old wooden stairs to
the kitchen to boil the kettle for coffee, intending to
start stripping yet another wall of its many generations
of wallpaper. But as she sipped the hot, reviving brew,
she realised for the first time since buying the house
just how very quiet it was—eerily quiet. A pin dropping in the attic would have shattered the silence. She
was annoyed to feel a tiny prickle of unease as she
glanced round the big farmhouse kitchen—what on
earth was happening to her now? Surely she couldn't
suddenly be afraid of being alone? That had never

happened to her in her whole life before. But then, she recalled wryly, nor had stage fright. No—it wasn't fear of being alone she was experiencing, she realised with a hollow pang inside—it was something much more basic than that, but just as alien to her character. She was lonely. She, Aurora Jennings Blake, who had always been quite content in her own company, who indeed had positively longed for solitude on occasions, was lonely.

She gave an undignified little snort. Well, she couldn't really blame this one on Adam Burns. He might be directly responsible for taking away her pleasure in singing—though that would surely be only a temporary aberration on her part—but she could only hold him to account for her loneliness if it was his company she was missing. And that she most certainly was not, she told herself adamantly. Frankly, she could survive in great happiness for a very long time without ever setting eyes on him again.

So why the loneliness now? Her features creased into a frown as she puzzled the mystery. And why the sleepless night? Eventually she gave a shrug. Some questions simply had no answers—and she had apparently found two of them. She was wasting time trying to rack her brains, and if there was one thing she hated doing, it was wasting time.

Laying down her coffee mug with a decisive thud, she got to her feet and strode with her usual long-legged grace to the dining-room. A couple of hours of hard graft should see it ready for the next stage of its facelift, and might also tire her out enough to get some sleep. It was worth a try.

She needed a plan of action, she decided as she began the task of stripping several layers of wallpaper from the walls—a concerted campaign to protect the club, and if she were to be painfully honest, herself, from the marauding hands of the so-called Midnight Raider. Business had been good in the few weeks she had been in charge, but she was astute enough to realise that many of the customers had been coming to the club simply to see her. Somehow she'd have to make sure they kept on coming after the novelty of her fame wore off.

'Forewarned is forearmed, Mr Burns,' she said grimly. 'Now I know who you are, I can take you on at your little game. The Midnight Raider isn't going to steal my club away!'

'Candy! Get your lazy body out of bed and get dressed. I'm coming over to pick you up.'

'You're what?' The voice at the other end of the phone sounded sleepily confused, and Rory grinned. Candy had never been a morning bird.

'You heard,' she returned heartlessly.

'What time is it?'

'Nearly eight-thirty. High time you were up, anyway.'

'Whaa-at? It's still the middle of the night! Go away and let civilised people sleep, can't you?'

'Not on your life. I've got things to do and I need your help to do them.'

A long heartfelt groan echoed along the line. 'Oh no, not another Aurora Blake brainwave—please, anything but that!'

'I'll see you in half an hour. Get the kettle on.'

Almost exactly half an hour later, Rory was sitting cross-legged on Candy's floor, grimacing as she took a sip of coffee.

'Why is it that you're the only person in the entire world who can't follow the instructions on a jar of instant coffee? This tastes awful!'

Candy shrugged. 'At this ungodly hour of the day you're lucky I even managed to find the right jar. I could quite easily have used gravy browning instead.'

'I'm not so sure you haven't,' Rory muttered wryly.

Candy shot her a baleful glance. 'You shatter my precious hours of rest with a phone call, demand that I get out of bed and then insult my coffee-making skills. What exactly did I do to deserve a so-called friend like you?'

A broad grin lit up Rory's features. 'I don't know, but it must have been pretty good!'

The other woman shook her head bemusedly, sending her tousled red curls tumbling about her face. 'What on earth has got into you this morning?' she said wonderingly. 'When I left you last night you were positively down in the dumps; today you're— you're. . .' she made a helpless gesture with her hands, searching for the right adjective '. . .you're sizzling! What happened? Did Adam Burns call you?'

'Did what?' The question pulled Rory up short, freezing the smile on her lips. 'Don't be ridiculous! You don't honestly believe he's got anything to do with the way I happen to be feeling, do you?'

'Well, he did the other night,' Candy pointed out with ruthless candour. 'He wrecked your act with a few well-chosen words that would have slid straight off your back if anyone else had said them. Explain that away if you can.'

'He simply took me by surprise, that's all,' Rory muttered. She picked absent-mindedly at a piece of lint on one long denim-clad leg, unable for the moment to look into her friend's probing blue eyes. She'd never been able to lie to Candy—the other woman knew her too well, could see through her straight away.

'Well, I'll be. . .' Candy rocked back on her heels, her arms folded in front of her, a look of astonished revelation on her pert features as she nodded knowingly.

'You'll be what?'

'I think I'll be astounded, that's what I'll be.'

Rory sighed heavily. 'Look, Cand, are you going to tell me what the heck you're talking about, or do I have to play riddle-me-ree for the next few hours?'

'It's finally happened, hasn't it?' said Candy.

'What has?' Rory frowned uncomprehendingly.

'A man's finally got to you.' A delighted twinkle danced in the cornflower-blue eyes. 'I was beginning to think you were truly immune—I actually thought the man hadn't been born who could get under your skin. But I was wrong!' Candy gave a little crow of laughter. 'And what a man—Adam Burns, of all people!'

To her fury, Rory felt the heat of intense embarrassment flooding her cheeks. 'Don't be ridiculous,' she returned hotly. 'I don't even like him!'

'I'm not at all sure that's a necessary ingredient— not in the early stages, at least. In fact, it might even be a hindrance, though I suppose later on you'd need to discover some kind of friendship too, otherwise what on earth would you talk about at nights?'

'Candy!' Rory held both hands over her ears to drown out the flow of apparently inane chatter. 'Look, I didn't drag you out of bed to talk about Adam Burns, or about any other man, come to that.'

'You see? You can't even bear to talk about him! Doesn't that tell you something?'

Rory nodded. 'Yes. It tells me I can't bear to talk about him! For the love of Mike, Candy, will you please get off my back about Adam Burns? He means nothing to me—less than nothing.'

'Who was it who said something about the lady arguing too much?'

'Protesting,' Rory corrected wearily. 'The quote you're trying to mangle uses the verb "to protest", but in any case it doesn't fit in this instance.'

'No?' Candy raised a disbelieving eyebrow, and Rory clenched her hands in an agony of frustration. What did she have to do to convince her?

'No,' she said at last with exaggerated patience. 'No, because I can assure you with hand on heart that Adam Burns is neither under my skin nor even anywhere remotely near it. If I'm protesting, it's simply because you're infuriating me beyond belief right now!'

Completely unruffled, Candy grinned broadly. 'For the second time in two days I'm hearing the usually benevolent lioness growl,' she said. 'Makes quite a refreshing change.'

'She'll do a whole lot more than just growl if you don't shut up and listen!'

Candy made a show of pressing her lips together and sat back expectantly, a mischievous twinkle still dancing in her eyes.

'That's better,' said Rory, only faintly mollified. 'Now—I've decided we should do something special at the club.'

'What sort of something special?'

'Give me another two seconds of silence and I'll tell you! What I've got in mind is a party—no, not a party—an event.'

'For the customers?' Candy was clearly intrigued.

'No—for local disadvantaged and handicapped children. We can get names from the council's social services department. We'll have it at the club, of course, lay on the full works for them, food, music, balloons—you name it.'

'I like it.' Candy nodded slowly, her active mind already racing ahead. 'What made you think of it?'

Rory shrugged. 'I've had something like it in mind ever since I sang in that charity concert last year. To be honest, it's not entirely altruistic—I thought if we put on enough of a show we could attract the media, get some publicity for the place. But it's for me too—I got such a buzz out of seeing the kids' faces at that show. They seemed to enjoy the whole thing a hundred times more than your average blasé concert-goer.' Her expression grew pensive. 'Anyway, I've been so lucky in life I reckon it's about time I started giving something back—and the club's the perfect place to do it.'

'So what exactly have you got in mind?' asked Candy.

'I'm not really sure yet. That's why I wanted to haul you in—I thought we could have a brainstorming session together.'

'At this time of the day?' Candy groaned loudly. 'It's asking a bit much of my brain even to be compos mentis, let alone capable of storming anything.'

'Drink some more of that foul coffee,' Rory suggested heartlessly. 'If that doesn't kick-start you into life, nothing will!'

CHAPTER FIVE

RORY stretched her arms high above her head, groaning pleasurably as the knots eased out of her aching muscles. After spending the better part of the morning crouched down painting skirting-boards, she felt as though she'd been put through a mangle. Still—she stood back to view her handiwork with a pleased nod— she hadn't done too badly for a total amateur, even if she did say so herself. And now she deserved a coffee break.

Clad in an old black leotard and leggings, now fairly well daubed with paint, and with her mane of hair hidden beneath a scarlet bandana, she didn't exactly look like a decorator, she realised with a giggle as she caught sight of her own reflection in the hall mirror on the way to the kitchen, but she'd discovered at an early stage of the game just how much bending, stretching and crouching was involved and so had decided she might as well be comfortable while she did it.

The only snag with decorating was that it had kept her hands busy, but left her mind all too free to wander. And over the past few days it had developed an infuriating habit of wandering unerringly back to the subject of Adam Burns. No matter what she did to distract herself, his dark penetrating eyes lingered in her memory as though they'd been branded there.

He hadn't even been in the club the previous evening, which should have helped but hadn't. In some ways it was easier having him around where she could at least keep an eye on what he was doing. In his absence she'd been as nervy as a wildcat, jumping a mile every time someone spoke to her or touched her on the shoulder, expecting him to turn up out of the blue as he'd made a habit of doing.

Damn and blast the man—he was going to drive her crazy if she wasn't careful. She'd have to find some way to forcefully evict him from her thoughts, and the only way to do that was to fill her mind with something completely different—like the party she was planning. With a resolute nod she reached for the telephone. No time like the present for getting things in motion. She tapped in the number of her agent, spoke briefly to his secretary, then held the receiver several inches away from her ear, knowing from past experience that Bernie could generally be heard for miles without the benefit of a phone.

'Babe!' The familiar whisky-edged voice came bellowing down the line, and she grinned fondly. 'Grown tired of playing manageress, have you? Ready to come back to the unreal world?'

'No, Bernie. I want a favour.'

'A favour?' The voice grew instantly guarded, but Rory wasn't fooled by it. In a business where agents were known for their sharklike qualities, Bernie had an endless struggle to conceal a naturally generous heart. Unfortunately for him, Rory had seen through the bluster within minutes of their first meeting, though she'd faithfully promised to keep his secret.

'A favour.' Quickly she outlined the plan, explaining that the party was to be for local children who were handicapped or disadvantaged in some way. 'And I want you to supply the icing on top of the cake.'

'You want a donation towards it all?'

Rory could practically see him reaching for his cheque book.

'No, Bern,' she cut in swiftly. 'It's not money I want—it's Ace Elliot.'

She heard his swift, incredulous intake of breath. 'Blimey, you don't want much, do you? Only the hottest thing in the charts, that's all!'

'Correct,' she returned calmly. 'Nothing but the best, that's my motto.'

'That's all very well,' he grumbled, 'but how am I supposed to swing it?'

'The same way you "swung it" when that charity show committee decided it wanted me on its bill,' she said. 'Remember?'

'Sure I remember. But that was different.'

'In what way?'

'You were a soft touch.'

She chuckled delightedly. 'Nope. You just got round me, that's all. No matter how hard I tried to steel myself, you just became more and more persuasive. Till I couldn't hold out any longer. So—will you do it? Deliver the big one for me?'

Bernie sighed gustily. 'I'll try. But you'll really owe me one if I succeed.'

'You'll succeed. And then I'll love you even more than I do already, if that's humanly possible.'

She was still laughing softly as she laid the phone down, but the laughter died in her throat as she looked up to see Adam standing a few feet away, his eyes hard as jet.

'My God, how do you do that?' she demanded crossly. 'You're forever creeping up on me—is it against your religion to knock on doors?'

'I've found I can discover a great deal more by

simply walking in,' he returned grimly. 'What's "the big one", Aurora? And who's going to deliver it?'

She bridled at his autocratic tone. 'I don't believe that's any of your business.'

He took a couple of strides towards her, and it was all she could do not to cower away.

'I'll ask you again,' he said quietly, but with an underlying threat in his voice that sent a shiver along her spine.

'And I'll tell you again,' she returned with a bravado somewhat at odds with the way she was feeling. 'It's none of your business.' She was infuriated by his arrogant assumption that he could simply demand answers, infuriated still more by her own desire to simply cave in and tell him the truth. She was a lioness, wasn't she? Surely a Leo was more than a match for a Scorpio, no matter how deadly its sting. One look in those mesmerising night-dark eyes was enough to make her doubt that.

She sighed heavily. She just wasn't equipped to deal with this kind of cold war. For the first time in her life she realised just how little opposition she had ever had to face—in anything. Her looks and her vibrant personality had always won the day for her—but perhaps in the long run that hadn't been a good thing, because now those weapons had failed her she was floundering, rudderless.

'Oh, all right,' she muttered ungraciously. 'It's just something I've got in mind for a big party I'm planning.'

'Party?' Adam's expression grew no less unfriendly. 'What sort of party?'

'For children. The ones who don't usually get parties.'

'Why didn't you explain that straight away?'

Because you put my back up with your cool assumption that I should simply tell you anything you want to know. Because I'm already vulnerable enough where you're concerned and for my own sake I have to hold on to some degree of control. But even as the words echoed in her brain, she knew she wouldn't voice them, wouldn't give him the satisfaction of knowing just how childishly he could make her behave.

He pulled a high stool from beneath the breakfast bar, the denim jeans he was wearing tightening over his muscular thighs as he sat down. Rory swallowed hard, horrified by a giddying little rush of longing. How could she feel desire for a man who infuriated her as much as this one did? It completely beggared belief, yet it was an inescapable fact. He was sitting just a matter of inches away, when he moved to reach for a coffee-cup she caught the smell of freshly washed hair, and her fingers itched with the memory of tangling themselves in those jet-black waves.

'Do help yourself,' she said, annoyance at her body's traitorous response making her surly. 'What are you doing here, anyway? Why do you seem to feel it's absolutely imperative to dog my every footstep?'

His smile didn't reach his eyes. 'What's wrong, Aurora? Did you get out of bed on the wrong side this morning? Or is the strain of running a nightclub finally beginning to get to you?'

'Certainly not!' Needled by the suggestion, she glared back at him. 'I'm perfectly capable of doing the work I'm doing—and a lot more besides.'

'Who are you trying to convince—me? Or yourself?'

If she really was trying to convince anyone, it was probably her father, Rory realised, but she wasn't about to hand Adam that kind of ammunition on a plate. He mustn't ever know that her father's faith in her capabilities was less than rock-solid, because he would doubtless use that as one more negotiating ploy in his campaign to buy the club.

She eyed him warily, her tawny-coloured eyes narrowing. 'Just why do you want this club so much anyway?' she asked abruptly. 'Surely there must be plenty of others you could target.'

He nodded. 'No doubt. But I want this one.' His eyes roamed lazily over her face and she had to steel herself not to look away. 'And believe me, Aurora, I always get what I want.'

She licked her lips nervously, managing with an effort to suppress a shiver. He meant what he said—and more. The predatory glcam in his eyes told her in no uncertain manner that he wanted her too.

She gave an uncaring little shrug. 'Then you'd better brace yourself for disappointment, because this time you're going to be unsuccessful.'

'You think so?' A faintly mocking smile played over his lips. 'And just how do you propose to stop me from getting what I want?' He leaned closer to her till she could feel the warmth of his minty breath on her skin. 'After all, you're a pussycat, Aurora—aren't you?'

'Cats have claws!' she hissed back at him, made deeply uncomfortable by his closeness.

He smiled. 'But they also like to be stroked.' As if to prove his point he drew one long finger over her cheek, trailing it over her bottom lip, his eyes glinting reprovingly when she tried to bite. 'Naughty little puss!' The finger moved relentlessly downwards, over her throat, through the valley between her breasts, but never quite touching them, then up over her ribs, tantalising, teasing her. She should stop him, should grab that exploring finger, but something within her refused to give him the satisfaction. Then his hand slid across to cup the underside of one full breast, and she gasped, too taken aback by the sheer exquisiteness of his touch to mask her reaction.

'You see, Aurora,' he murmured, 'I was right—you do like to be stroked.'

She'd been robbed of words, had no speech to tell him to stop this glorious torture, could only groan deep in her throat as his questing fingers flickered over one nipple, bringing it to prominent life even through the material of her leotard.

'You have no right to do this to me,' her voice emerged from a strangely constricted throat sounding even huskier than normal.

'Your body's giving me the right,' he said, blatantly dropping his gaze to her breasts. 'No matter what your mind might be telling you right now, Aurora, your body is begging for more of my touch.'

'What do bodies know?' She made a valiant bid to shrug away from him, but it made no difference. 'You're obviously an experienced man, you know how to elicit a response. My body's simply reacting to that.'

His lips twisted mockingly. 'So you'd react this way to the touch of any "experienced man"?'

She flinched, caught in a trap of her own making. 'Certainly not! Despite what you seem determined to think, I am not and never have been promiscuous.'

'But you are passionate.' He leaned closer still, his warm breath ruffling through her hair and she had to fight against an almost overwhelming desire to lay her head on his broad shoulder and feel his arms close around her. 'My Aurora, you are one very passionate woman.'

'I am not "your Aurora",' she tried to protest, but it was hard, so hard, when she was having to fight as much against herself as against him.

'Not yet,' he murmured. 'But you will be.'

The softly spoken threat cut through the haze fogging her brain and she sat bolt upright, knocking away the hand that had been caressing her into submission almost without her realising it.

'Never!' she swore vehemently. 'You'll never have the club, and you'll never have me. You can't make me do anything against my will!'

Amusement glinted in his eyes. 'I won't have to.'

Suddenly desperate to put a distance between them, Rory jumped down from the stool to pace restlessly round the kitchen like a caged animal, unhappy in its imprisonment.

'People like you make me mad!' She swung back to face him, her hands planted firmly on her hips. 'You've obviously chosen to believe your own publicity—you like the idea of being a "Midnight Raider". You've probably never encountered opposition before, because you've deliberately gone after the weak who couldn't fight back. Well, this time you've met your match, Adam Burns. I'm not about to keel over for you!'

The skin seemed to grow taut over his cheekbones, making him look more predatory than ever.

'I ought to put you over my knee for that,' he gritted out. 'You deserve a good spanking—just like every other spoiled brat.'

'I what?' She all but yelled the words at him, incensed beyond reason that he could even consider such a thing. No one had ever raised a hand to her in anger, and woe betide him if he should decide to be the first man to try. 'Don't even think about it, or you'll. . .'

'I'll what?' There was a strange glitter in his eyes as he blatantly goaded her. 'I'll live to regret it? Is that what you were about to say, Aurora? Do you truly believe I would?' His gaze swept lazily over her, making her squirm, then with one swift movement he caught her by the wrist, pulling her so abruptly towards him that she stumbled, caught off balance.

'Let go of me!' She threw her head back defiantly. 'I'm giving you one final warning, Adam—if you touch me I won't be held responsible for my actions!'

His laughter echoed mockingly round the room as he raised his hand to her head and pulled the scarlet bandana free.

'That's better,' he murmured approvingly as her gold curls tumbled about her shoulders. 'I like to see my women with long beautiful hair.'

'If I were your woman, God forbid that I should ever be so cursed, I'd cut all my hair off!' she hissed back through gritted teeth, devastatingly aware of the effect his nearness was having on her traitorous body. Left to their own devices, she knew only too well her arms would even now be snaking up round his neck, her lips parting to invite his plundering mouth.

'You think so?' Utterly ignoring her struggles to free herself, he slid one hand beneath her hair to cup the back of her neck, and pulled her face to within a couple of inches of his own. 'Ah, what a pair of lovers we shall make, my Aurora!'

'Never!' Keeping her voice steady was a battle in itself as the touch of his hard, powerful body against her own was sending her breathing awry. 'I'll never be your lover. You can't force a response from me.'

'I don't intend to.' He dipped towards her, and she tried again to free herself, but the more she struggled, the more his fingers tightened their hold on the back of her neck, and she closed her eyes helplessly, steeling herself for the marauding touch of his mouth. But where she had expected harshness she felt instead only the soft warmth of his lips on her throat, and a rush of longing coursed through her entire body, strong enough to make her buckle at the knees. Only his strong arms holding her tight against him saved her from falling, her bones turning to liquid within her as his lips nuzzled relentlessly towards her ear.

She was horribly aware she was being manipulated, knew his cynical tactics for what they were, yet she was powerless to resist, and when his mouth traced a line of feather-like kisses across her cheek her lips parted of their own accord, begging for their share of the richness. At last, after what seemed like an eternity of waiting, his mouth took possession of hers and she whimpered deep in her throat, pressing closer to him, her breasts flattening against the solid wall of his chest. Nothing else mattered any more, nothing else in the entire universe held any significance except the man holding her with such quiet strength.

At last he raised his head, and with a feeling of dread she searched for the triumph she was sure she must see now in his eyes. But after a long moment he shook his head.

'I didn't do that to prove some sort of mastery over you,' he said evenly, and she drew in her breath sharply, wondering if he read her mind. 'I did it because I wanted to make you look the way you do now.'

'And how do I look?' She'd intended to make a

sharp retort, but even to her own ears her voice sounded tremulous, full of longing that hadn't been satisfied.

He smiled. 'Dewy-eyed, flushed, like a woman who's been held and kissed and wants to be kissed again.'

'I don't!' But even as she made the token protest she knew a longing almost painful in its intensity to feel the possession of his mouth all over again. Sweet heaven, what was he doing to her? What was this spell he was casting—and how could she ever hope to be free of it? Those few moments in his embrace had shown her all too clearly just how vulnerable she was where he was concerned. Suddenly the idea of keeping her enemy close seemed ludicrous—how could she keep him close when she fell apart at the seams every time he was anywhere near her?

'You may think you can lie to me, but you can't go on lying to yourself,' he said with calm assurance. 'You won't be able to fight those passionate fires raging within that beautiful body of yours forever.' His eyes regarded her steadily. 'But I'm the only one who can light those fires, Aurora—and I'm the only one who can quench them.'

She stared back at him in wide-eyed horror, still weakened by the desire he had ignited, horribly afraid he might be speaking only the truth. She would have loved to have laughed in his arrogant face, but the way she was feeling right now the laughter would have strangled in her throat.

'I would like you to leave now,' she said, managing with a supreme effort to make her voice steady. 'As you can doubtless see, I'm in the middle of decorating, or rather I was when you barged in and interrupted me. I really don't want to waste any more time, so if you don't mind. . .?'

'As I recall, you were actually in the middle of a phone call when I arrived,' he said evenly. 'And since you were apparently too engrossed in it to hear my knock at the door, I simply let myself in.'

'Ok, Ok.' Rory looked away, too weary to argue any more. 'In any case, what I said still stands. I'd be grateful if you'd just go.' She sent him a faintly ironic sideways glance. 'As Candy would no doubt tell you, anything that stays still for too long around here gets painted or wallpapered.'

'I'll risk it.'

'What?' Her eyes widened in surprise. 'But. . .'

'I'll give you a hand. Decorating's a tiresome enough chore without having to do it all on your own.'

'You don't have to. . .'

'I know I don't have to,' he said calmly. 'I've volunteered to. Go and get me a brush.'

CHAPTER SIX

FOR a long moment Rory could only stare at him, totally nonplussed. What was he playing at now? Adam Burns might be many things, but she doubted if 'handyman around the house' was one of them. It just wasn't his style. If he ever needed such domesticated chores done, he'd doubtless hand the job over to the most exclusive interior decorator in town. So what was behind this? Her eyes narrowed suspiciously.

'Why?' she asked bluntly.

'Why what?' Amusement flickered briefly in his obsidian eyes.

'Why are you offering to help?'

Adam shrugged. 'I've got nothing better to do.'

'No nightclubs to buy? No new midnight raids to organise?' she said a touch sarkily, and the amusement faded from his eyes, to be replaced by irritation.

'Do you always respond to offers of help like this?'

'No, but then I don't usually have to wonder what's going on in the mind of the person who's made the offer,' she returned.

'Then you should,' he said drily. 'Haven't you heard there's no such thing as a free lunch?'

'So what's the payment in your case?'

'It would seem, the dubious pleasure of spending time with a shrewish and ill-tempered woman,' he told her.

'"Shrewish woman"!' Her temper sprang back into vivid life as she all but shrieked the words back at him, her fingers unconsciously curling themselves into the fists she'd dearly love to use on him. She'd never resorted to violence in her life, but suddenly the thought of landing a punch square on that granite jaw was enormously appealing. Surely that would finally crack his glacial front?

To her still greater fury, his lips curved into a blatantly mocking smile as he nodded towards her clenched hands.

'Feel like going a round or two, do you, Aurora? I'll give you a fair fight if that's what it takes to cool that hot head of yours.' He lifted his hands, beckoning with both forefingers. 'Come on, what are you waiting for?'

She could do it—not with her fists but with the techniques learned in martial arts. Just a few simple, subtle moves and he'd be lying on his back wondering what on earth had hit him. And the temptation to try out all she'd learned was suddenly overwhelming. Then in her mind she heard an echo of the words her teacher, a martial arts master, had used time and time again.

'When I give you knowledge of these skills, I also give you a heavy responsibility,' he had said. 'You must never use them in attack, only defence.'

At the time it had been easy enough to make the pledge he had demanded, since she hadn't been able to imagine a situation where she would ever want to attack anyone. But that had been before she had met Adam Burns! For a moment she wavered, torn between the desire to finally get the best of him in something, and the equally strong need to stick to her word. At last her conscience won out and she gave a tiny sigh, wishing not for the first time that she could, just occasionally, be a touch more ruthless.

'I wouldn't give you the satisfaction,' she said, tilting her chin scornfully.

She had expected an equally sarcastic reply. Instead his lips twitched slightly in what might or might not have been a smile.

'Shame,' he said softly. 'I think I'd quite enjoy a tussle with you.' His gaze swept boldly over her and she felt a rush of warmth right through her veins as though his hands had followed the path taken by his eyes. Stunned by the sensation, she had to search for all the willpower she possessed not to let her reaction show in her expression.

'Well,' she said at last with only a faint betraying tremor in her voice, 'if you really are dead set on staying to help, there is something you could do.' And if the task she had in mind didn't send him rushing from the house, she was a Dutchman.

The gleam in his eyes told her he was ready for the challenge.

'Just name it.'

'Very well. I've got a ceiling just waiting to be painted.' With a faintly malicious grin she nodded towards the dining-room. 'Unfortunately the village stores didn't run to non-drip, so I hope you won't mind the odd splash here and there. I'm afraid I don't possess any overalls.'

'So I've already gathered from your own choice of decorating gear,' he murmured, once again letting his eyes roam freely over the leotard and leggings clinging lovingly to her like a second skin.

'I'll get you a paintbrush,' she muttered, all but taking to her heels in her haste to get away from those penetrating eyes. At the hall cupboard she stopped, taking a deep steadying breath to calm the currents

suddenly eddying through her body. What on earth
was it about him that he could make her come unglued
with just a single look? Heaven knew she was no
stranger to men's admiring glances, but they'd never
had this effect on her before—nor anything remotely
like it! And just how was she supposed to stay aloof
when her wayward body kept ignoring the commands
of her brain?

'Get a grip, Aurora,' she told herself sternly as she
rummaged in the cupboard. 'You may as well accept
that he's going to be around for a while—until he
finally accepts that the club's not for sale. That's going
to be hell on earth if you keep dissolving into a mushy
heap every time he so much as looks at you.'

Marginally more in control, she sauntered back
through to the kitchen and handed him the brush,
carefully keeping her own fingers clear of his. Right at
this moment his touch would probably disintegrate her
completely.

She was surprised to discover he was perfectly adept as
a painter and decorator—though why she should be
surprised she didn't really know, she reflected a touch
grouchily as she watched him work. Adam Burns was
probably good at everything he turned his hand to. If
she'd done the job herself she'd doubtless by now be
sporting more paint then the ceiling, but he'd managed
to avoid almost all the splashes. Either that or the paint
had simply been afraid to sully his obviously expensive
jeans and sweatshirt. Rory couldn't suppress a soft
chuckle at the thought, and he looked down from the
stepladder at the sound.

'Is something amusing you?'

She shook her head. 'I was just thinking that this is

a most unexpected setting to find the Midnight Raider in.'

He smiled, and her eyes snapped wide open in genuine astonishment.

'I've never seen you do that before!' she exclaimed.

'Do what? Paint a ceiling?'

'No. Smile—a real honest-to-goodness ordinary, human smile. You should do it more often.' Or perhaps he shouldn't, since it had made her heart give an enormous, inexplicable leap. That smile had afforded her a fleeting glimpse of another side of Adam Burns— a side that was warm and humorous. For her own sake it was a side she couldn't afford to see too often. To her relief he ignored the comment.

'You wouldn't think it so unexpected if you'd seen the first nightclub I bought.' Now his smile had a wry edge to it. 'There was no money left over for niceties such as professional decorators.'

'So you did it yourself?'

He nodded. 'All of it. After first removing many years' worth of nicotine from the walls, that is.'

Rory shook her head in amazement. She'd been so sure he'd been born to money. The clothes he wore, the cut of his hair, even the subtly elegant watch on his wrist, everything about him seemed to indicate a man who had been brought up to take wealth for granted.

'So you're a self-made man?' she said abruptly, suddenly realising just how little she knew about him.

Adam raised a querying eyebrow. 'You make it sound like a disease,' he said mildly. 'If you mean that I worked hard to make my own money, then yes, I did. I still do.'

'At the expense of others.' She bit her lip as his expression turned glacial all over again. Just for a second there, she'd been uncovering a softer, more human side to the man. But she'd blown it with that acidic little crack. She was surprised to discover how much that hurt.

'What the hell is that supposed to mean?' he demanded.

She gave a tiny shrug. 'Just that you've apparently cornered the market in finding weak and easy targets, people who have neither the strength nor the wherewithal to fight you.'

'You've clearly made up your own mind about me,' he said coldly. 'I don't see much point in trying to alter such a bigoted outlook.'

'Bigoted?' Rory was stunned by the description. She had always prided herself on her tolerance and open-mindedness—how dared he call her bigoted? Because that's the way you sounded, a tiny voice said in her brain, and she turned away, sick at heart, unable to deny it. He brought out the very worst in her, she realised numbly. In his presence she was constantly on the defensive, and that made her uncharacteristically prickly. He'd been right when he'd said she was shrewish, though she'd never suffered from the malady before.

The worst of it was, she couldn't even afford to apologise, couldn't take the risk of opening up to this dangerous man. She had already discovered to her cost just how strongly attracted she was to him on a physical level. If she found herself liking him—and several times during the course of the afternoon's decorating she had come perilously close—she could never hope to keep up her side of the battle to keep the club.

Doubtless that was all part of his master plan, she thought, deliberately stiffening her resolve against an insidious desire to unbend a little. He probably worked on all his victims this way—softening them up, earning their trust and then moving in for the kill. Such subtlety would be true to form for a scorpion, after all. And, when she came to think of it, he might have disliked her description of him, but he hadn't denied any of it.

He finished painting in a silence so icy she could almost feel its frosty fingers on her skin, then climbed down the ladder and handed her the paintbrush.

'You may think of me what you will,' he said coldly. 'Your opinion means less than nothing to me. But I suggest you attempt to overcome your own immature outlook on life long enough to consider what's going to be best for the club. Remove those blinkers you seem determined to wear where I'm concerned—for your father's sake if nothing else. I'm not a particularly patient man, Aurora. My offer to buy won't last forever. And he won't find a better one.'

'He won't need to,' she said staunchly. 'He doesn't want to sell.'

'You don't want him to sell, you mean,' he said. 'Because for the time being you're apparently enjoying your new little game of manageress. But what happens when you grow tired of it, Aurora—what happens when the novelty fades and you find yourself longing to get back to the bright lights of show business? What happens then?'

'*If* it happens,' she returned, placing a heavy emphasis on the first word, 'my father will once again pick up the reins of control.'

'Whether he wants to or not.' Adam made it a statement rather than a question.

She looked away from his penetrating dark eyes. 'He will,' she muttered.

'You're sure you know him well enough to make that claim with authority?'

She glanced up. 'Know him well enough?' she echoed incredulously. 'He's my father!'

He shook his dark head. 'That doesn't necessarily mean a thing. People often misunderstand those closest to them.'

He was doing it again, she thought with some amazement—putting her on the spot and forcing her to examine things she'd always taken for granted. OK, her relationship with her father had taken a dip since her mother's death, but she still knew the man better than almost anyone else on earth. Didn't she?

She frowned as questions began to whirl in her mind. She had assumed all along that the only reason her father could possibly have for even considering selling the club was concern that she, Rory, couldn't cope with running it, that it would prove too much of a burden for her—that it would hold her back from her own career. But what if she'd been wrong in that—what if there were other things he wanted to do? He wasn't getting any younger, after all, and he'd been a hard worker all his life. Suddenly she realised the direction her thoughts were taking and shot Adam a furious look. He'd laid a trap for her and she was on the verge of plunging headlong into it.

'How dare you?' she snapped angrily. 'How dare you presume to tell me what's good for my father? You don't care about him—you don't care about anything but yourself and your own empire-building mania. Well, you've picked the wrong target to home in on this time, Mr Burns! I'm strong enough to take you on—and beat you—at your own devious little game!'

His expression remained as unchanged as if she'd

never spoken, and she was gripped all over again by a longing to shatter that icy exterior. Just what did it take to get through to this man?

'Have it your own way,' he said evenly. 'If you're determined to be so pigheadedly stubborn and blind to the truth, so be it.'

'Blind to your version of the truth, perhaps,' she shot back, incensed. 'And long may I remain so.' She took a deep breath, desperately trying to steady the anger churning within her. 'Now, if you don't mind, I really must get cleaned up and ready for the evening ahead. I've got a club to run.'

His dark eyes gleamed. 'For the moment,' he said in a soft voice that sent a shiver along her spine. 'For the moment.'

'Business is slow tonight.'

'Well, it's only Tuesday. What do you expect?'

Candy held up her hands as if warding off a blow. 'Don't bite my head off,' she said. 'I was merely passing a comment, that's all.'

Rory sighed heavily as she let her eyes roam over the sparsely populated dance floor. 'Sorry—I'm a bit touchy on the topic of the club right now.'

'Why? It's doing pretty well in general, isn't it? The takings aren't down or anything, are they?'

Rory shook her head. 'They did take a dip last weekend,' she admitted.

'Because you didn't sing,' Candy said shrewdly. 'That's why.'

'Surely not?' A frown creased Rory's brow. 'I can't believe the customers have been coming just to hear me.'

'Maybe not for that alone, but you've certainly been

a big draw,' the other woman said. 'You only have to listen to people talking about you at the bar to realise that. You've always been hugely popular.'

Till Adam Burns put his spoke in the wheel. Rory grimaced, remembering with more than a touch of bitterness Candy's original theory that Adam had tried to spoil her pleasure in singing because on stage she was public property, and he wanted her for himself. The memory was made more bitter still by the fact that she had come close to believing it. Hah! Well, she knew better now. It wasn't Rory Adam had set his sights on, it was the nightclub, and it seemed now that his first devious move was already paying dividends in loss of business for Rory. If that trend continued, her father would definitely lose what little faith he had in her abilities. She couldn't even hope to keep that from him, since he'd insisted she fax him details of the takings every week.

'Surely the answer's obvious enough,' Candy broke into her train of thought. 'Just start singing again.'

Rory shook her head abruptly. 'I can't let the success of the club stand or fail on my stage appearances,' she said. 'It has to have firmer foundations than that.'

'In other words, you still haven't got over your attack of stage fright,' Candy said shrewdly. 'Well, you'd better find some way of getting over it, my girl—you won't be managing the club forever.'

Rory turned away. She still hadn't admitted to the other woman that she wasn't at all sure she'd be returning to the music business. How could she tell her when she still had so many doubts in her own mind about the path she was going to follow in the future? Then she groaned heavily, catching sight of the all too familiar figure of Adam Burns approaching.

'You again,' she said darkly, deliberately injecting hostility into her voice, at the same time resolutely squashing the ridiculous little spurt of pleasure she had felt on seeing him. Pleasure? Was she losing her mind?

'Good evening, Aurora,' he said civilly. 'If you're this welcoming to all your customers I'm not at all surprised you're losing them.'

She bristled angrily. 'Don't you have anything better to do than waste your time where you're not wanted? Like running your own nightclubs, for example.'

He smiled coldly. 'My clubs are in good and capable hands,' he said. 'Which it would seem is more than could be said for your father's.'

At Rory's side Candy was following the exchange, her eyes growing wider with every barbed comment.

'Ding, ding,' she said with a mischievous grin. 'End of round one. Can I sell tickets for round two? This sounds like being the prize fight of the year!'

Rory shot her a black look. 'Don't you have something useful you could be doing?' she said pointedly.

'No. But I'm sure I can find something,' she amended hurriedly, seeing Rory's eyebrows draw together threateningly. 'Nice to see you again, Adam.'

It didn't help Rory's mood one iota to see a conspiratorial grin flash between Candy and Adam before the other woman scuttled away.

'How refreshing to see that you believe in fostering good relations between management and staff,' he drawled lazily. 'So very important to the smooth running of the clubs, I've always found.'

'Did you want something, Adam?' Rory asked coldly. 'Or have you simply come here to annoy me?'

His eyes narrowed. 'As a matter of fact I've come here to tell you something,' he said shortly. 'Are you going to listen—or do you intend to keep up this childish prattle for the rest of the night?'

She closed her eyes, steeling herself against another flare of irritation. 'I'm listening.'

'Not here. In your office.'

She wanted to refuse—would have given anything to simply walk away and leave him standing there. But her curiosity wouldn't allow it, and he knew that, blast him. Incensed by her own lack of willpower, she turned on her heel and marched towards the office, indignation clear in the ramrod straightness of her spine.

'Well?' As the door closed behind them she turned to him, hands planted on hips, her chin tilted defiantly upwards. 'You have something to say?'

Adam nodded slowly. 'I do.'

'Then kindly get it over with.'

She could tell by the tightening of his lips that he didn't take kindly to being given orders, but he could hardly back down now since he'd been the one to insist they go to the office. For a fleeting second she allowed herself to revel in the unaccustomed feeling of having the upper hand over him. It was short-lived.

'Are you aware that a drugs ring is being operated in the club?' he asked abruptly.

His words hit her like a battering-ram, making her knees buckle beneath her. Quick as a flash he was at her side, catching her before she hit the ground, his arm hooking behind her knees to scoop her up into the air. For a moment she lost all sense of reality, her senses whirling dizzily, his solid bulk the only anchor in a world suddenly tipped off its axis. She was hazily aware of being set down in a chair, then her head was pushed none too gently between her knees.

'What do you think you're doing?' she protested weakly.

'Never mind, just take several deep breaths.'

With his hand cool and firm on the back of her neck holding her head in place, she could hardly refuse, and in any case it was sensible advice. After a couple of moments of deep breathing, the giddiness receded.

'All right,' she murmured, 'you can let me up now.' As his hand lifted from her neck she looked up.

'Did you say what I think you said a moment ago?'

'About a drugs ring?' Adam nodded grimly. 'Yes. Are you really so shocked?'

'Shocked?' She gazed back at him, her eyes wide and incredulous. 'Of course I'm shocked. I would never allow such a thing to happen in my father's club.'

'Meaning you'd allow it to happen elsewhere?' His dark eyes narrowed shrewdly.

'Certainly not! What do you think I am?'

'I know what you have been,' he returned shortly.

'Meaning?'

'Meaning that you've been heavily involved in a world known for its fondness for alcohol and drugs.'

'How dare you?' Rory leapt to her feet, her tawny eyes blazing with anger. 'Are you suggesting I've taken drugs?'

His expression never wavered. 'Have you?'

'Get out of my office!' she stormed. 'In fact, get right out of my life! I don't want you around me. You've caused me nothing but problems ever since you. . .'

'Ever since I first started making you question all the things you'd so happily taken for granted?' He eyed her coolly, totally unmoved by her outburst. 'Sit down, Aurora.'

The man's cool arrogance took her breath away.

That he could sit there so calmly, issuing orders as if she were a naughty schoolgirl, simply beggared belief.

'I asked you to leave,' she said, the effort of reining in her anger making her voice tremble.

'And I told you to sit down.' A wintry smile played about his features. 'One of us is going to have to give way, Aurora. Which one will it be?'

She closed her eyes, mentally counting to ten, desperately trying to calm the inferno raging within her. At last she sat down, her expression hostile but tightly controlled as she looked at him.

'I'm prepared to hear you out,' she said through gritted teeth. 'Drugs are a very serious issue—and you're quite right, I have been involved in a world where they're common currency. But in answer to your highly impertinent question—no, I most certainly have not ever taken drugs, and never will.'

'Habitual users are also accomplished liars.'

'In heaven's name, what do I have to do to get through to you?' Frustration splintered her veneer of control. 'Do you have any reason whatsoever to doubt that I'm telling you the truth—other than the fact that I'm a singer? That's nothing more than circumstantial evidence—even you can't brand me guilty on that!'

He nodded slowly. 'True. But I've been watching you closely over the last few weeks, Aurora. You're given to some very strange mood swings.'

'Mood swings?' She gazed at him uncomprehendingly. Now what on earth was he talking about?

'I've seen you on stage, vibrant, full of life, totally in command. I've seen you on that same stage hesitant, unsure of yourself, struggling to get by.'

Because of you. Because of you and the things you said—you were the one who robbed me of my confidence. She wanted to scream the words back at him, but they log-jammed in her throat. To reveal the truth would be to render herself still more vulnerable to him, and she couldn't allow that to happen. But the alternative—to have him believing her poor showing had been caused by drugs, was equally untenable. She was caught between a rock and a hard place—with no obvious way out.

'Everyone's entitled to an off night,' she muttered at last.

'Do you have them often?'

'No, but. . .'

'And then there was the day I arrived at your home,' Adam went on relentlessly. 'You disappeared into the farmhouse at the rate of knots.'

'To make iced tea!' Rory shook her head disbelievingly, beginning to wonder if she was in the middle of a crazy dream. Surely she couldn't really be having this ridiculous conversation? 'Are you suggesting I went into the house for some other reason? Like a quick fix, perhaps?'

'You live in a very remote place,' he said obliquely. 'If you were so inclined you could get up to all sorts of things without anyone knowing about it.'

'If I were so inclined, then yes, I suppose I could,' she conceded. 'But I'm not! How on earth can I convince you of that?'

'Does it matter to you that I should be convinced?'

'Yes, of course it does!' she all but yelled back, then bit her lip. Dammit, she was doing it again—letting her mouth speak before her brain was properly engaged. 'It would matter to me if *anyone* suspected me of taking drugs—not just you.'

He rested his elbows on the arms of the chair,

steepling his fingers beneath his chin as he regarded her. 'I'm convinced,' he said quietly.

'You're what?' Now she was completely thrown. 'You mean you believe me?'

He nodded. 'I too have my contacts in the music business, Aurora. Your reputation for being totally clean is practically a legend. You couldn't possibly have maintained that if it weren't true.'

She slumped back in her chair, strangely deflated as though all the fight had suddenly gone out of her. 'Then what was all that about? Why have you been giving me such a hard time for the past ten minutes?'

Adam smiled that wintry little smile she was beginning to recognise. 'I suppose in a way I was testing you,' he explained.

'Testing me? For what?'

'To see just how strongly you'd react. I needed to know how you felt about the whole topic of drugs.'

She stared at him wonderingly, totally unable to fathom out this incredibly complex man. 'Why didn't you simply ask me?' she said.

'I did. In my own way.'

Which was the way he would always do things, she realised. Adam Burns was very much his own man, following no dictates but his own.

'Well, now you do know,' she said. 'I hate the things—and I utterly condemn those who deal in them.'

'So how do you feel about the fact that a ring is currently operating in the club?'

She shook her head vehemently. 'I don't believe it.'

'Then you don't know the place as well as you think you do.'

'I know it a damn sight better than you do!' Feeling

her temper begin to rise again, Rory made a concerted effort to rein it in. 'Are you honestly trying to suggest that a drugs ring could be operating right under my nose without my knowledge?'

'I'm not suggesting it,' he said calmly. 'I'm stating a fact.' His expression thawed fractionally. 'Look Aurora, this proves the point I've been trying to make all along. You may sincerely believe yourself capable of running a nightclub, and as far as the public relations and administration side goes, that's probably true.'

'Thanks for the backhanded compliment,' she muttered grouchily.

'But there are things you have no experience of,' he continued inexorably as if she hadn't spoken. 'And this is obviously one of them.'

'No experience? But you said yourself just a few moments ago that I've been involved in a world where drugs are common currency.'

'And you took great pains to stress that you've steered well clear of them,' he pointed out. 'Therefore you're not likely to recognise the danger signs.'

She sighed heavily. There was just no winning with this man. To every argument she put forward he would inevitably find a counter, and she had no doubt that could go on forever. Suddenly she was weary of the constant battle between them. Unthinkingly she looked up at him, her eyes taking in the powerful width of his shoulders, the incredible contained strength of him. She'd felt that strength when he'd scooped her easily into his arms. She was no lightweight, yet he had lifted her as though she were thistledown. For one aching, unguarded moment she wished she were back in his arms, nestled against his hard body. Then she mentally gave herself a shake—steeling herself against the creeping rush of longing.

'I don't know what kind of game you're playing,' she said in a low voice. 'This place is clean—I'm certain of it.'

'Certain enough to risk the club on it?'

'Risk the club?' Her voice lifted an octave. 'What on earth do you mean?'

'I mean, Miss Blake, that I have enough information already to go to the police, information which could be enough in itself to warrant the club being closed down.'

Here eyes widened in shock. 'Closed down?' she echoed. 'You can't be serious!'

'I've never been more serious in my life,' Adam said grimly. 'And believe me, I won't hesitate to do it.'

She dropped her eyes to the desk, staring unseeingly at the ledger lying on the polished wooden surface. It was a nightmare. She was caught in the middle of a terrible ghastly nightmare, and one she couldn't even hope to escape from by waking up.

'Are you trying to blackmail me, Adam?' she said, her voice strained and hollow. 'Is that what this is all about? If I don't persuade my father to sell you the club, you'll manufacture enough fake information to make the police suspicious enough to close me down?'

When he didn't answer immediately she glanced up at him, and the breath caught in her throat at the look of barely controlled fury in his night-dark eyes.

'You stupid little fool!' he grated savagely. 'What we're talking about here is something infinitely more serious than the club. People's lives could be at stake, or at the very least their futures. Can't you see far enough beyond your own petty little desires to realise that?'

Rory shuddered, shaken to the roots of her soul by the undisguised venom in his voice. 'Why is this so important to you?' She had to force the words past a badly constricted throat.

He shook his head impatiently. 'That doesn't matter for the moment. What does matter is you. I've already taken a considerable risk by telling you this much. If you choose to, you can blow this whole thing sky-high, just with a few words to the wrong people.'

Hurt showed clearly in her tawny eyes as she gazed back at him. 'I'd never do that,' he said vehemently. 'I still think you're totally wrong, but I'd never do anything that could endanger you—or the club.'

'Good.' He smiled in quiet satisfaction. 'Then come and dance with me.'

CHAPTER SEVEN

'I REALLY don't think that's necessary,' Rory began firmly, remembering the last time he had held her in his arms on the dance floor.

'Come on, Aurora— we're two adults, and, whether you like it or not, we're in this thing together now. Surely we can conduct it in an adult manner?'

'Oh, very well,' she capitulated. 'Only this time we'll dance according to the music.' That should ensure her safety, since the disc jockey inevitably stuck to the same pattern of fast music at this stage of the evening, keeping the slow, romantic records for the end of the night.

'Fine,' said Adam.

Rory led the way to the disco floor, all too aware of the speculative glances slid in her direction from the other dancers, yet aware too of a peculiar little thrill of pride as she caught the envious looks in the eyes of the other women. Adam Burns was a stunningly attractive, charismatic man, even she could never deny that. Then her eyes snapped wide open in amazement as the funky disco beat changed to a slow, sensual ballad.

'How did you do that?' She glared at him accusingly.

His returning smile was blatantly mocking. 'I didn't do anything,' he said softly. 'You're the one who pays the DJ's wages.'

'Are you suggesting I asked him to play slow music?' she shot back, outraged.

He shrugged. 'You made the condition that we dance

according to the music,' he reminded her. 'I merely agreed to it. How fortunate for us both he didn't decide to play the Highland Fling!'

Try as she might, Rory couldn't help but giggle at the ridiculous picture that conjured up in her mind's eye. And when he held out his arms to her she stepped forward into his embrace, knowing full well she would only attract more interested looks if she refused. Refused—hah! Who was she trying to kid? As soon as his arms closed about her, her body nestled into his as though it belonged there, and just for a moment she allowed herself to lay her forehead against his shoulder. She could no more have refused the lure of his embrace than metal could resist the pull of a magnet.

Unconsciously she slid one hand up his back to twist her fingers in the jet-black hair brushing the collar of his jacket.

'I'm relieved to see slow-dancing with me hasn't turned out to be the traumatic experience you obviously feared.' The faintly mocking tone in his voice forced her back to reality, and she snatched her hand away from his hair as though it had come into contact with burning oil.

'I simply forgot myself for a moment, that's all,' she said stiffly. 'Blame it on the music.'

'Then blame this too.' Almost before she had time to realise what he had in mind, Adam lowered his head to hers and she swayed helplessly in his arms, weakened all over again by the incredible sweetness of his mouth. The man was such a devastating mixture, she thought hazily, outwardly so cold and enigmatic, but revealing in his kiss a passion so potent it thrilled her to the depths of her soul.

It would be so easy to give up the battle she'd been

waging against him, simply to lay down her arms and give herself up to the ecstasy of possession. But to do that would be to risk being enslaved for ever. In many ways she was her father's daughter, and she knew he had only loved one woman—her mother. It would be the same for Rory—she'd always known she'd give her heart only once, and that was why she hadn't played the love game with the same reckless abandon as so many of her contemporaries.

The thought brought her up short, and she pulled away from his kiss, sending him a quick horrified glance as she wondered once again if he had been able to read her mind. What on earth was she thinking about—she could never fall in love with him! The man she'd dreamed of was strong, just as Adam was strong, but he was compassionate too, and full of gentle humour. In fact, he was as far removed from Adam Burns as summer was from winter.

'Penny for them,' he murmured, stroking one warm finger along her cheek, and the caress made her quiver deep inside. Sweet heaven, what was happening to her? She knew what this man was, knew he was capable of raiding hearts just as easily as nightclubs, yet here she was all but melting away because he'd touched her! She had to get a grip on her ridiculous emotions, had to keep reminding herself that it was only the club he wanted. Rory would be nothing more to him than a pleasant extra thrown in for good measure.

Steeling herself, she tilted her chin to give him an aloof, autocratic stare. 'I was just thinking about your foolish and utterly misguided belief that there's a drugs ring in this club,' she said coldly.

His features hardened. 'Would you like to say that again, perhaps a little more loudly this time?' he said witheringly. 'The couple next to the loudspeaker didn't quite hear you.' He shook his head wonderingly as he looked down at her. 'Are you so afraid of being wrong that you're prepared to put up warning notices for those involved?'

She glowered darkly back at him. 'There's no need to do that,' she returned, but more softly this time. 'Because there *is* no one involved. Except perhaps in your dark and suspicious mind.'

He tightened his hold on her and she gasped involuntarily, knocked off balance all over again by the hard strength of his body pressed so close to her own. But there was no warmth in his embrace, and she shuddered as his eyes narrowed threateningly.

'Be very careful, little girl,' he warned. 'You could end up playing with fire.'

'I can look after myself,' she returned sullenly.

'I hope for your sake that's true. Because when I start to shake this vipers' nest, a great deal of evil could come crawling out. And you're going to have to be strong enough to cope with it.'

Shaken to the core by his words, Rory could only stare at him, her eyes large and haunted. Then he dropped his arms as the music changed back to a funky disco beat, and without his support she stumbled, only just managing to catch herself in time before she fell against him. Numbly she followed him from the dance floor, barely even noticing when some of the dancers called out to her in passing. Back in her office, she turned to him, her features drained of colour.

'You really are serious, aren't you? You're not kidding about the drugs ring?'

His mouth tightened into a grim line. 'I never kid about anything,' he said shortly. 'If you thought I was simply playing a little game, then you can think again, Aurora.'

She nodded. 'I still don't believe it's true,' she said, her voice barely audible. 'But you were right when you said drugs were a serious issue. And despite what you seem to think, I don't see this as a game either. If there is a drugs ring operating in my father's club, then I'll help you to crack it in any way I can.'

She wasn't sure how she had expected him to react to her announcement—gratitude or admiration might have been a bit much to hope for, she acknowledged wryly, but even a faint hint of relief would have been something. Instead, he just gave a little nod.

'Good. Then let's sort out a time to sit down and start comparing notes.'

'Notes?' She sent him a mystified glance. 'But I don't have any notes. I've never seen anything suspicious in the club.'

'Perhaps you have without realising it. Just think about it and then talk to me, Aurora—let me judge whether you have anything worth saying.'

'Again, Aurora—from the beginning. Tell me what the club was like when you first took over.'

Rory gazed at Adam through weary, incredulous eyes. 'When I said I'd help you in any way I could I didn't expect you to turn into Torquemada!' she said bitterly. 'We've been over this a hundred times already. How many more times will it take before I can convince you I haven't seen or heard anything remotely suspicious?' She slumped back against the armchair, exhaustion seeping into her very bones.

She'd been shaken rudely out of sleep by the sound of peremptory knocking on the back door of the farmhouse, at what felt like the crack of dawn. She had all but crawled downstairs to answer the imperative summons, yawning as she tugged open the door. But all thoughts of sleep had fled instantly at the sight of Adam standing on the doorstep, his features grimly determined.

'What on earth are you doing here at this time of the morning?' she demanded sleepily.

'Why, who were you expecting?' His eyes dropped blatantly downward and she remembered with a start that she was wearing only a flimsy nightdress, barely skimming the tops of her slender thighs.

Feeling the heat of his gaze right through the thin material, she folded her arms protectively, realising only when she saw his mouth curve into a mocking smile that she had merely pushed her breasts upwards, making them clearly visible above the ribbons and lace of the bodice.

'Oh, for goodness' sake!' Flustered, Rory turned her back on him and all but ran for the kitchen. 'You wait here,' she threw back over her shoulder. 'I'm going to put some clothes on.'

'Pity,' he murmured. 'I was enjoying the view.'

The sound of his low mocking laughter followed her as she took the stairs two at a time, desperate to be away from his gaze, all too aware that a scarlet flush had enveloped her entire body—aware too that the heat he had generated in her hadn't only been embarrassment. Damn him! How could he do this to her—forever turning up when he was least expected and always managing to catch her at a disadvantage? Doubtless that was all part of the game he played, she thought irritably as she ransacked the wardrobe for something to wear. What she needed right now was something cool and elegant, something with poise and sophistication that would at least restore a fraction of her dignity.

She caught sight of her own reflection in the full-length mirror behind the wardrobe door and gave a disgusted snort. The way she was looking right now, pink-cheeked and with her hair falling about her in tousled, tangled curls, it would take a miracle to transform her into elegant and sophisticated. Hearing the sound of his footsteps at the bottom of the stairs, she quickly pulled on the first things that came to hand—a pair of well-worn jeans that clung lovingly to her like a second skin, and a sweatshirt. With a grimace she grabbed her hair and twisted it into a knot on top of her head. She was a million miles removed from poised and elegant, she reflected ruefully—but at least she was decent.

'Now, Adam,' she re-entered the kitchen with her chin tilted defiantly upward and a challenging glint in her tawny eyes, 'what's so important that it couldn't wait till a more reasonable time of day?'

'The future of the club,' he returned calmly. 'Unless of course you don't consider that to be important?'

'Well, of course I do,' she shot back, irritated to find herself wrong-footed yet again.

He gave a single nod. 'Good. Then pour yourself a coffee, sit down and start thinking.'

'Thinking?' She frowned quizzically. 'About what?'

'About everything that's happened since you took over the club. And I mean—everything.'

Glancing at the clock on the wall now, Rory realised to her amazement that he'd only been in the farmhouse for three hours. It felt more like three weeks. He hadn't let up for a single moment, questioning, probing, searching for clues in her answers like a scientist searching for new bugs on a microscope slide. Again and again she had told him there was nothing she could say that would help him, but he refused to be distracted from his goal.

'You could at least try to help by giving me a clue as to what sort of thing I might have seen,' she grumbled.

Adam shook his head. 'I don't want to put ideas into your head.'

She threw up her hands in irritation. 'Well, at least tell me why you're so all-fired sure that there is a drugs ring in the club, then! I've already told you I've never seen any signs of one—and nor have any of the staff.'

'Are you sure of that?'

'Well, of course I'm sure!' She glared back at him, nettled that he should even ask such a thing. 'They'd have told me if they suspected something was going on.'

'Unless they happened to be a part of it.'

'What!' She shot him a horrified look. 'What on earth are you suggesting now?'

'Nothing very much out of the ordinary,' he returned calmly, unmoved by her outburst. 'It wouldn't be unusual to find the staff—or at least some members— active participants. Who better?'

'But some of them have been here for ages,' she remonstrated. 'With the exception of Candy, who came with me, they were all hand-picked by my father. He'd never employ anyone involved in drugs.'

'Not knowingly, perhaps. But dealers don't wear placards proclaiming their trade.'

She shook her head vehemently. 'He'd have known. He can pick out a charlatan at a hundred yards.'

Adam's lips quirked humorously. 'Then he's an

astute man indeed,' he said solemnly. 'But no one's perfect. We can all be fooled.'

Rory pushed herself out of her chair, suddenly fuelled by restless energy, and strode to the window, gazing unseeingly over the lawn for a few moments as anger seethed within her. Then she turned back to him, placing her hands on her hips, unconsciously squaring up to him. 'All right then, Mr Adam Burns, if you're so convinced my staff are part of this alleged operation, then prove it. Name names. Don't just throw empty accusations around!'

His eyes narrowed. 'Are you going to indulge in histrionics like this at every turn, Aurora? Because if you are I'd better count you out of the reckoning right away. If you really do want to help me, I need your unquestioning support, not your childish tantrums every time I do or say something you don't like.'

'My "unquestioning support"?' She echoed his words incredulously. 'Just what do you think I am, Adam—a robot?'

'No.' Annoyance glittered darkly in his eyes. 'Since unlike you I don't make a habit of placing people in neat little labelled categories.'

His answer left her floundering helplessly. He'd done it again, she realised in amazement—with just a few choice words he'd knocked her for six. But then she'd practically loaded the gun that had shot her down and handed it to him. When would she learn to censor her impetuous tongue? Determined not to present him with any more ammunition, she paused for a long moment, considering her words carefully before trying again.

'Very well, Adam,' she said with exaggerated slowness. 'I've promised to give you my assistance, and my support. But I won't promise it'll be unquestioning, because I refuse to relinquish my right as an intelligent human being to question everything I don't understand or accept.'

For just a second she thought she saw a flicker of admiration in his eyes, but it was gone in a flash, leaving her to wonder if she'd simply imagined the look.

'Very well,' he said gravely. 'You drive a hard bargain, but I'll go along with that.'

She had a strong suspicion he was laughing at her, but for the moment decided to let it pass. Right now there were more important issues at stake than her offended dignity.

'Good. Then perhaps you'd be good enough to answer the first of those questions,' she said.

He gave a nod of assent.

'Several moments ago I asked you why you thought there was a drugs ring operating in the club,' she said. 'So far I haven't heard your answer.'

'I was given the information,' he told her, 'by a young man who's horrified by what his brother has become because of drugs. He heard on the grapevine that I was interested in this place, and came to me, not without considerable risk to himself.' He paused thoughtfully. 'He told me your club was one of the main places in the operation.'

Rory was staggered by his answer. She'd been so sure he'd say he was acting on instinct or following up some vague, unsubstantiated rumour—she'd never anticipated anything so concrete, or so damning.

'Why did he come to you rather than me?' she asked, through lips grown strangely dry.

'Because he knew I would help,' he said shortly.

'And he thought I wouldn't?'

Adam shrugged. 'You're a rock star. You could have been involved in it up to your neck.'

'But I'm not!' she protested.

'He didn't know that.'

Rory closed her eyes briefly. 'But why you?' she said again.

'Because he knew it was important to me. And don't ask why again,' he held up one hand. 'Just accept what I've said.'

It went against the grain to meekly obey, but the look in his eyes told her in no uncertain terms that she was standing on the edge of a minefield.

'Then why didn't you go straight to the police with what he'd told you?'

'Because he couldn't give me names, only descriptions. I was afraid that with such incomplete information the police might get to the monkeys involved—in other words, the front men, without reaching the organ-grinder himself.'

'And you think you can do better?' Her lips twisted scornfully. Was there no limit to the man's arrogance.

Her sarcasm drew no visible reaction. 'On this occasion, yes,' he returned calmly. 'Drug barons frequently seem to have a sixth sense where the police are concerned. They can spot an investigation before it's even been properly launched. But they have no reason to suspect me.'

'Thanks to me,' Rory returned, unable to keep an edge of bitterness from her voice. Just for a second she wondered if she was being taken for a complete fool. She had agreed—no, worse than that, she had volunteered, to help him in something which could ultimately lose her the club. But what else could she have done?

she reasoned silently with herself. She couldn't bear the thought of such an evil trade operating on her territory, but she could never have hoped to crack it herself.

Candy would tell her there was no point in trying to buck fate—it was in the stars that she should become entangled in this whole crazy situation. Fair enough— but why had the planets been cruel enough to land her in partnership with the one man in the universe who could drive her crazy with wanting, even as he was— well, just driving her crazy!

'Yes, thanks to you,' Adam agreed.

'What would you have done if I'd refused to help?'

His expression remained unchanged. 'I'd have gone it alone.'

'Even with all the risks?' She knew the answer to that one without even asking the question. Adam Burns was a hard man to get to know, but one thing she was instinctively sure of was that he'd never back away from something simply because it was dangerous. Unconsciously she gave a little shiver. He'd be a good man to have on your side—but as an enemy he'd be more lethal than the Scorpion of his star-sign.

'Any more questions, Aurora?'

She shook her head wearily. 'Not for the moment.'

'Then we can get back to mine.'

She shot him an incredulous look. 'You have more? It's not possible, Adam! You've practically taken me through every minute of every day since I took the club over. You already know I don't have anything to tell you.' She took a deep, steadying breath. 'Look, why don't I phone Candy and ask her to come over? She's been at my side ever since I started managing the place. Perhaps she's seen something suspicious.'

Adam shook his head. 'No. This has to stay between you and me. No one else must be involved—it's too dangerous.'

'But Candy's my best friend,' she remonstrated. 'She would never give the game away.'

He was adamant. 'We can't take the risk. I don't believe she could keep her mouth shut. Candy's too open, too honest.'

Rory stiffened visibly at the implied insult. 'And I'm not?'

His lips curved in a barely perceptible smile. 'Let's just say you've got more at stake. 'Now, let's start again. From the beginning.'

'Are you losing weight?' Candy's blue eyes narrowed suspiciously as she prowled round Rory like a tiny bird of prey inspecting its dinner. 'You are losing weight! You're not on a diet, are you?'

Rory made the best attempt she could at a dismissive laugh. 'Don't be ridiculous! When did you ever know me to go on a diet? I enjoy my food far too much.'

'I know that,' Candy returned ruefully, 'and it's always been the bane of my life that you can eat your way through a tuckshop without gaining a pound while I only have to look at a picture of a cream cake to make the scales groan.' She stopped in mid-prowl, tapping one finger thoughtfully against her lip. 'But you just don't look your usual picture of glowing health right now. There are even violet shadows beneath your eyes! You've never had those before, not even when we've been on tour.'

Rory suffered her scrutiny in silence. What could she say—that, since her promise to help Adam, her whole life had been turned upside down? That she'd lost her normally very healthy appetite, reduced to picking desultorily at meals where once she would have tucked in hungrily? That she hadn't been sleeping properly, finding herself tossing and turning, ending up with twisted sheets and pulverised pillows? That she'd lost the ability to concentrate on anything longer than two minutes at a time? Candy would think she'd lost her mind. And she probably wouldn't be far off the mark either, Rory realised grimly.

'It's Adam, isn't it?' Candy said suddenly, making her start in surprise.

'I don't know what you mean.'

'Don't give me that!' Cornflower-blue eyes bored into her own and it took all the willpower she possessed not to look away. 'He's got you tied in knots.' Candy shook her head wonderingly. 'Would you credit it—all these years I've wondered how on earth you've managed to avoid falling in love, given all the glorious hunks you had to choose from, just falling over themselves to be near you. But if this is what love does to you, it's perhaps just as well you've never suffered from the malady before.'

Rory shook her head, sending her long wheat-coloured curls tumbling about her face. 'Don't be ridiculous,' she said adamantly, then bit her lip. She was caught between a rock and a hard place here, she realised with grim humour. Since Adam had been monopolising practically all her time, she couldn't protest her dislike of him too vehemently. Candy would pounce on that like a terrier, demanding to know why she didn't just tell him to get lost. But she'd given her promise, albeit with great reluctance, not to confide the truth to her friend. 'Adam's a fascinating person, of course,' she stumbled inelegantly over the words, 'but I'm not in love with him.'

'Could have fooled me.' Candy pressed her lips together knowingly. 'In fact, I'd go as far as to say you've got the worst case of it I've ever seen.'

'Thanks very much for the diagnosis, Doc,' Rory returned wryly. 'But you're way off the mark. Now— are we going to get on with planning this party, or are you just going to sit there and make stupid remarks?'

Candy shrugged. 'Suit yourself. You can deny it to me all you like—I just hope you're not trying to deny it to yourself.'

'There's nothing to deny!' Rory shot back hotly. 'Now will you please get off my back!'

The other woman stared at her for a long moment, then, with great dignity, collected up the papers lying on the desk in front of her and got to her feet.

'I've also never known you to shout at me,' she said quietly.

Horrified that she could have been so thoughtless, Rory laid a beseeching hand on her arm. 'Don't go,' she said softly. 'I'm sorry I shouted. You're right, of course—it *is* Adam. I don't know whether I'm on my head or my feet with him, and it's kind of hard to cope with.'

Candy smiled and patted her hand. 'It's all right, sugar. It's just hitting you harder than most because it's taken you longer than the rest of us to discover the joys and the agonies of falling in love. Your body doesn't know what's happening to it, that's all.'

Wasn't that the truth? Rory reflected gloomily as Candy sat down again, her momentary anger placated. She'd never experienced anything like this in her life before—she'd never met a man who had made any

real, lasting impression on her. Oh, yes, she'd had
relationships—light, amiable things that gave her
pleasure while they lasted, and no pain when they
ended. What she had now with Adam couldn't even be
called a relationship, she acknowledged ruefully. They
were partners of a sort—more often than not, sparring
partners, as her hot-headed impetuousness clashed
with his icy resolve.

And yet there were times, fleeting but strangely
precious times, when he seemed to momentarily forget
the war of nerves raging between them. Times when
he would absentmindedly lay his hand on her shoulder,
or stroke a wayward curl from her cheek. Whenever
he did, it was as though a bolt of red-hot lightning
streaked through her body, reducing her to a quivering
jelly. She knew all too well he meant nothing by it,
that he probably hadn't even noticed he was doing it,
but she still found herself hoarding the memory of each
insignificant caress as a miser would hoard gold.

She had repeatedly told herself her response to his
touch was nothing more than a temporary aberration
on her part, that familiarity must inevitably breed
contempt, that sooner or later she would feel nothing
more than irritation. It hadn't happened yet. Finally,
infuriated by her own weakness where Adam was
concerned, she had turned on him one evening in the
club, shaking his hand from her hair as though scorched
by his touch.

'Why do you keep doing that!' she snapped.

'Doing what?' If he was surprised by her outburst,
he didn't show it.

'Touching me.' She knew her words sounded petu-
lant, but she couldn't help it.

Amusement briefly quirked the corners of his mouth. 'Is my touch so objectionable to you?'

'No! Yes! I don't know—it's not that, but. . .' totally unaccustomed to being tongue-tied, Rory glared at him darkly. Now he was turning her into a stammering schoolgirl! 'I just want to know why you keep doing it, that's all,' she finished lamely.

Adam shrugged. 'People have probably begun to wonder by now why I spend so much time in the club,' he said evenly. 'I decided to put them off the scent.'

For a moment she could only stare at him, completely at a loss as to what he meant. Then the penny dropped, and her eyes widened in horrified shock. 'You're trying to make them think you've been coming in to see me? That there's something going on between us?'

He smiled lazily. 'Got it in one.'

She'd turned her back on him then and stormed away, her back ramrod-straight, so angry she could barely see straight. For two pins there and then she would have summoned the two black-jacketed men who stood sentry on the door every evening, ready to eject any troublemakers. It would have given her infinite satisfaction to watch Adam being frogmarched to the door. But even as she fumed she could see the sense in his ploy—nobody would be suspicious of his frequent presence in the nightclub if they thought he had something going with Rory. If she felt hurt at the realisation that his affectionate gestures had been no more than a front—well, it could only be because her ego was wounded. Nothing more.

Thinking about that now brought a scowl to her features, till Candy waved a hand in front of her eyes.

'Hey, anybody in there?'

Rory snapped back to the present, smiling apologetically at the other woman. 'Sorry, Candy, I was a million miles away.'

'Your normal location these days.' Candy's cornflower-blue eyes searched her face. 'Look, Rory, has something been bothering you recently? Other than Adam, I mean? You know you can talk to me about anything.'

For a moment the temptation to simply unload everything was all but overwhelming. Keeping everything from her had been incredibly tough, particularly since Candy was highly adept at winkling out secrets, but Adam had been completely inflexible on the subject. She mustn't be told, he'd said. The risks were too great. Rory had fumed, unaccustomed to being dictated to, but his will had proved the stronger.

To put her off the scent and give her something else to think about, Rory had put Candy in charge of organising the children's party. The ploy had worked surprisingly well, especially when Candy had learned that Bernie had been successful and that Ace Elliot was to be the star guest.

'My God, Rory, he's gorgeous!' she'd breathed, her eyes shining large and lustrous. 'Don't you think so?'

Rory had been reduced to simply shrugging her shoulders in reply, stuck for an answer, and that had depressed her still more. Normally she would have found the tall blond rock star attractive, even if only in a detached, academic sort of way. But for some reason the thought of dark, obsidian eyes and a powerful, muscular body kept getting in the way. What on earth was wrong with her? Was she becoming obsessed with Adam Burns?

'Ye gods and little fishes, you're off again! Rory,

have you heard a single word I've been saying for the past five mintues?'

She started guiltily as Candy's accusing tones cut through her reverie. 'Of course I have!' She did her best to look indignant, at the same time trying to sneak a look at the paper Candy was holding. Surely that would give her a clue. 'You've been talking about wonder-boy Elliot,' she guessed, spotting his name.

'Wrong.' The other woman wagged an admonishing finger in her direction. 'I knew you hadn't been paying any attention. I was asking you about the guy Adam's been talking to this evening.'

'Guy?' Rory's attention was fully engaged now. 'What guy?'

Candy shrugged her narrow shoulders. 'I don't know. I've never seen him in before tonight.' She eyed Rory thoughtfully. 'I don't imagine he's anyone special, though. Do you?'

Well aware that Candy was fishing, Rory shook her head just a touch too decisively, then bit her lip. She really wasn't any good at this game of deception— especially where her friend was concerned. Sure enough, Candy's eyes narrowed shrewdly. 'Then why did you pounce like that when I mentioned him?'

'Pounce?' Rory gave a light little laugh. 'Don't be ridiculous! I was surprised you mentioned him, that's all. Now come on, let's get some work done around here. I take it you'll be willing to undertake the arduous task of looking after Mr Elliot and his inevitable entourage when they arrive?'

Having successfully diverted Candy, she mentally breathed a sigh of relief. The other woman had caught her completely on the raw with her mention of the man she had seen Adam with, though to be honest she

couldn't really have said why. Now questions started
buzzing round in her mind—who was he? Why had
Adam been speaking to him? Was he involved in the
drugs ring Adam was still convinced was operating in
the club?

Galvanised into action by the very idea, she rose
abruptly to her feet, striving to keep her expression
impassive as she glanced down into Candy's surprised
eyes.

'You carry on here,' she said. 'It's about time I took
a stroll round the club. I like to make sure the
customers are happy.'

'You'd make them a lot happier if you'd start singing
again,' Candy returned, going unerringly for the jugular. 'So when are you going to get over this ridiculous
attack of stage fright?'

Rory made a dismissive gesture with her hands. 'It's
not stage fright. I just don't feel like singing right now.'

'And birds don't feel like flying,' Candy snorted
inelegantly. 'Don't forget who you're talking to here—
I've known you a long time, remember? And I've seen
the look in your eyes recently when you've been
watching the singers on stage. You're longing to get
back up there, only something's holding you back.
Surely you can't still be bothered about Adam's ridiculous gibe about you being brash and brassy?'

Rory winced, still sensitive to the cruel words. Candy
was right, she realised bleakly—part of her did want to
get back where she belonged, and there was nowhere
she felt more at home than on a stage. But she was still
bearing the scars of that horrendous night when she
had stood in front of the audience feeling bereft and
alone. She couldn't face that again.

'Just leave it for now—OK, Cand?' she said lightly.

'It's nice to let other people have their shot too—I'm quite happy to be a member of the audience for a while.'

'Sure you are.' The other girl made no attempt to hide her disgust as she turned back to the books lying before her on the table, and Rory felt her spirits sink still further as she headed for the door.

She spotted Adam almost as soon as she entered the club, but though he was sitting only a short distance away with a stocky sandy-haired man she didn't recognise, it took her some time to reach his table, since she was obliged to stop at every few strides to talk to customers. When she finally reached his side, he looked up, his eyes dark with an anger he wasn't quite quick enough to conceal.

'Hello, Aurora,' he said, standing up courteously to greet her. Only she could have heard the vein of ice underlying the apparently welcoming words. 'I thought you were busy in the office.'

'I was.' She smiled towards his companion, who gave a cool nod in return. 'Aren't you going to introduce me to your friend?'

'It's about time I was going, Burns.' The other man rose abruptly to his feet. 'I only popped in because I'd heard you were in town.' His cold, strangely fishlike gaze wandered blatantly over Rory and she managed only with an effort not to shudder. 'Now I can see why you're here.' His smile was more of a leer, and unconsciously Rory took a step nearer to Adam's powerful frame. He put one arm about her shoulders.

'Yes,' he returned tonelessly, 'I'm a lucky man.'

The sandy-haired man's eyes narrowed as he took in the possessive gesture, but he made no comment on it. 'I'll be in touch,' he said.

As he walked away into the crowd, Adam muttered a particularly earthy curse beneath his breath, and Rory looked at him in amazement.

'I've never heard you swear before,' she said. 'What brought that on?'

'You did.' His voice was low, too low for anyone else to hear, but it's tone was biting.

'I did? How?'

He grasped her suddenly nerveless fingers in his hand, sending her a smile with enough voltage to make her weak at the knees. It was only for the benefit of anyone who might be watching, she reminded herself grimly, but she couldn't ignore the tremor of longing deep within her, a longing almost too strong to contain.

'Come and dance with me,' he said, and his fingers cut into her tender flesh as he grasped her arm.

'But. . .'

'Don't argue.'

Numbly Rory allowed him to lead her to the dance floor, moving automatically into his arms as though she'd always belonged there. She'd lose all of this soon, she realised bleakly. Fate had thrown them together, but eventually their paths would separate, leaving her with nothing more than the memory of a powerful body pressed close and warm against her own. She should be longing for that day to come—should be ticking off the seconds till she was free of him again. Instead—unthinkingly she moved closer to him, sliding her fingers into his hair as though she could somehow capture the feeling to keep forever.

'You're a fool, Aurora.' His voice whispered like satin over her hair, yet all she heard was its underlying harshness.

'What?' She gazed back at him, confusion mingling with hurt in her expression.

'You heard.' His lips were smiling lovingly, but his eyes were hard and unfeeling as jet. 'The way you just came barging over just now—you could have blown everything I've been working towards sky-high.'

'Who was he?' she demanded. 'Who was that man you were talking to?'

He stroked one finger along her jawline and she suffered exquisite tortures under the false caress. 'Someone who may be able to lead me right to the heart of the operation,' he said softly.

'Then how could I have spoiled things?'

'Probably entirely by accident,' he returned. 'Luckily he didn't stay around long enough for you to inadvertently put your pretty little foot in it.'

She shook her head. 'I don't understand.'

Adam casually glanced about, nodding briefly to one of the regular customers dancing a few feet away from them. Then his hands slid down over her back, making her gasp as he pulled her body still closer to his own.

'What are you doing!' she snapped.

'Dancing with the woman I love,' he returned calmly. 'At least, that's what everyone here tonight must believe I'm doing.' He smiled tenderly, and the knowledge that he was only doing it for the benefit of anyone who might be watching sliced deep into the very heart of her.

'If you ever find enough human emotion to fall in love then I can only pity the victim from the bottom of my heart,' she said savagely, lashing out in her pain like a wounded animal.

'Why, Aurora?' That there was only amusement in his dark eyes added to her anguish all the more.

'If the way you treat me is anything to go by, she's in for a life of sheer hell!' she bit out.

Adam raised one dark eyebrow sardonically. 'But I'm not in love with you.'

'Thank heaven for that, because I hate you, Adam Burns!' She tried to rip herself away from him then, but his arms were like bands of iron around her.

'Careful, darling, people might be watching,' he murmured silkily.

'I don't care!' she snapped, too far gone in temper now to care about the consequences. 'Let them watch, let them see just what a despicable, unfeeling bastard you really are!'

'Unfeeling?' The single word murmured over her mouth, then his lips were on hers, and all the fury he'd aroused in her turned to fiery passion. She moaned deep in her throat, despising her own weakness, hating herself even as her lips parted beneath his, hungry for more of him. She forgot where they were, lost all awareness that they were surrounded by people, knew only a craving for his touch.

'Rory.'

Through dazed, clouded eyes she gazed up at him, the taste of his kiss still tingling on her mouth, her heart beating an erratic tattoo within her breast. Then reality returned with a rush as she suddenly realised that the music had stopped and that they were the only couple still left on the floor. Over the microphone the DJ gave a loud whoop of laughter.

'Well, folks, we may not have heard our favourite songbird sing for the last couple of weeks, but it's certainly nice to know our very own Rory can still put on one hell of a floorshow!'

Embarrassment more acute than anything she'd ever

known before rooted her to the spot as the sounds of laughter and applause rang out all around her. Then Adam squeezed her hand.

'Give them a bow, Aurora.'

For a second it was as though she were frozen, unable to move. Then the professional in her broke through, and seemingly from nowhere she managed to conjure up a smile. Deliberately making her movements large and extravagant, she swept into a curtsy, still holding Adam's hand, and the cheers grew still louder. Then, with a final naughty wink, she ran off the dance floor, and didn't stop till she reached the sanctuary of the office.

'Well done, Aurora! That was brave.' Adam had followed her.

'Brave?' She echoed the word incredulously. 'Brave? I've never been so humiliated in my entire life, and all because of you! How dare you make a fool of me in front of all those people?'

'I was kissing you,' he returned calmly. 'And as I recall, you were kissing me back. There was no force involved.'

That he was speaking only the truth simply served to infuriate her all the more. But even as fury blazed like an inferno within her, she knew it was directed at herself as much as at him. How could she have reacted like that to his touch?

'In fact,' he continued, 'I'd like to congratulate you. If anyone in the club had been left with any doubt that you and I are in love, that touching little display on the dance floor must have convinced them otherwise.' He gave a satisfied little nod. 'You're a much better actress than I'd ever have given you credit for, Aurora. Well done!'

And that, she realised with an increasing feeling of horror, was the whole awful crux of the matter. She hadn't been acting when she'd responded so passionately out there on the dance floor. The feelings she had displayed so publicly were anything but fake. She was genuinely—and, she very much feared, irrevocably—in love with Adam Burns.

CHAPTER EIGHT

DEVASTATED by the sudden realisation, she all but collapsed on to a nearby chair, her legs no longer capable of holding her up.

'What is it, Aurora—are you ill?' Adam's voice held a sharp note of concern and she looked up at him through dazed eyes, almost surprised to see him still standing there. She was about to shake her head, but changed it at the last moment to a nod. She had to get out of here, had to be on her own for a while, had to sort out the confusion fogging her brain. This was as good an excuse as any.

'I feel a bit strange,' she said.

He laid a cool hand on her forehead and she suffered new agonies beneath the touch of his fingers. 'You're burning up,' he said. 'Do you feel as though you have a fever?'

If the situation hadn't been so horrendous, his question would have made her laugh. She had a fever all right—only it wasn't the sort any doctor could treat. She shook her head.

'Probably just some sort of flu bug,' she said. 'A couple of the nightclub staff have already gone sick this week.'

'I'll take you home.'

'No!' She hadn't intended to sound quite so vehement, but what she needed most right at this moment was to put as much distance as was humanly possible between herself and Adam. She summoned up a weak smile. 'I'd really rather you stayed and helped Candy lock up for me. I can drive myself home.'

'Are you sure?' For the first time since she'd met him there was genuine warmth in his eyes, concern robbing his features of their normal granite harshness. She looked away, unable to cope with this unexpected new side to him. It was bad enough that she'd fallen in love with the cold, glacial man she already knew him to be—if she were to suddenly discover a tender, humane element to his character, heaven help her. She'd be sunk without a trace.

'I'm sure,' she muttered, getting rather unsteadily to her feet and reaching for her jacket. He took it from her and placed it on her shoulders, and she had to fight an urge to simply lean back into the solid warmth of his powerful frame.

'I can manage.' She pulled away from him, shrugging her arms into the jacket sleeves.

'There's no need to be so independent,' he said with mild reproof. 'Everyone can get ill. It's not a crime.'

'Everyone except you, I suppose!' she shot back accusingly, then bit her lip wearily, recognising her own tactics for what they were. She was deliberately trying to pick a fight with him because she was terrified he'd realise how she really felt about him. She couldn't cope with that, couldn't face seeing derision in those dark midnight eyes.

But what else could she possibly hope to see? she wondered miserably. He'd made it clear right form the start just how he regarded her—as a brash and brassy nightclub singer, nothing else. All the tenderness he'd shown her had been nothing more than a sham, just a front to convince the interested public that they were lovers.

Well, she couldn't even complain about that—he'd been upfront about his intentions, had never pretended to feel anything he didn't. She had no one but herself to blame if she'd fallen hook, line and sinker in love. She slid him a sideways glance, only to be all but felled by a wave of longing, and closed her eyes despairingly, swaying slightly where she stood.

'Aurora!' His voice pierced the mist swirling round her brain. 'Are you going to faint?'

It took everything she had, but she managed to shake her head. 'I'm fine.' She shot him a baleful look. 'I'm going now.'

'You're going nowhere.' His tone was calm, even, yet underlaid with tempered steel.

'And just how do you propose to stop me?' She jutted her chin pugnaciously as she glowered back at him, her pupils darkening in anger. 'Are you going to give me the macho caveman act? Drag me off to your lair by my hair, perhaps?'

Wordlessly he reached into his pocket and dangled a set of keys a couple of inches in front of her face. For a second she gazed at them, perplexed, then realisation dawned and she made a single vain lunge forward.

'Those are my car keys! How did you get them?'

'From your jacket pocket,' he returned mildly, moving his hand just a couple of inches clear of her grasp. 'You clearly aren't in a fit state to drive, but I assumed you'd be stubborn about it.'

She should have known—should have expected a scorpion to use subtle tactics. But how could she ever predict anything where this totally unpredictable man was concerned? Mentally she counted up to ten, desperately willing her temper to subside. She couldn't hope to achieve anything by exploding in his face all the time.

'Look, Adam,' she said at last, 'I admit I felt a little peculiar for a while, but whatever it was has passed and I'm absolutely fine now. So please, just give me my keys and I'll drive home and go to bed.'

'You're as white as a sheet,' he returned implacably. 'Your cheekbones are practically jutting out of your skin. You'll go home by taxi.'

'But then I won't have my car!' she shot back, losing the vestige of control she'd managed to achieve. 'I'll be stranded—in the middle of nowhere!'

His lips quirked in amusement. 'You chose to live there.' Then he shrugged his broad shoulders. 'I'll make sure it's returned safely.' He took a step towards her and instinctively she backed away, then stopped dead in her tracks, irritated anew by her own reaction and still more by the answering glint in his eyes. 'Come along, Rory,' he said softly, and the unexpected sound of her pet name on his lips sent a strange shiver along her spine. 'I'll walk you to the taxi rank outside.'

She was still pondering on his use of her name as the taxi drove through the dark city streets, the driver having given up on any hopes of conversation after a couple of monosyllabic and nonsensical replies from his customer. When they reached the old farmhouse she handed him the fare, absent-mindedly giving him a tip that was at least treble the size she would normally have made, barely aware of his delighted grin as she made her way towards the kitchen

Why had he called her Rory? Why now, when all this time he'd stuck rigidly to her real, rather austere christian name, had he suddenly switched to the softer-sounding Rory? Automatically she prepared to go to bed, her mind worrying at the puzzle like a terrier. She climbed between the cool sheets, pulling the covers up around her, then sat bolt upright, another memory drifting to the surface. He'd called her Rory earlier in the evening—when they'd been dancing, when he'd kissed her and made her completely forget she was in the middle of a crowd of people. She groaned, suffering all over again the excruciating embarrassment of those moments.

She lay down again, hugging the quilt around her as she closed her eyes, longing for sleep to overcome her, to give her some release from these endless, plaguing thoughts. Moments later she sighed exasperatedly—it was no good. She'd never get to sleep like this. She was too wound up, too much on edge, her nerves as taut as violin strings. And to cap it all she could feel the ominous beginnings of a thundering headache.

Muttering under her breath, she flung back the covers and swung her long legs out of bed, the flimsy material of her nightdress caressing her thighs as she padded barefoot to the kitchen to fetch a couple of aspirin. It took some time to locate the bottle— normally as healthy as a young animal, Rory rarely had need of medication. But these, she reflected with a wry smile, were desperate times. If she didn't get some decent sleep soon, she'd be in severe danger of cracking up completely under the strain.

'Oh, for goodness' sake!' To her annoyance the bottle was empty—belatedly she recalled making a mental note weeks ago to buy new supplies. Well, the way she was feeling right now, she'd have to find something to dull the edges of the pain, and to let her sleep. Perhaps a nightcap instead? She picked up a barely touched bottle of whisky from the dining-room table, frowning faintly as she studied its label. She wasn't much of a drinker either—didn't even particularly like the taste of alcohol, but she'd have to look on it as a necessary medicine.

With a fatalistic shrug she poured a generous measure of the amber liquid into a crystal glass, topping it up with lemonade. Since she hardly ever drank, she'd probably have a hangover to contend with on top of everything else come morning, but frankly it would be a relief to have something else to think about other than Adam.

Back in bed she sipped morosely at the whisky, grimacing slightly at its taste, then giggling wryly at her own reaction. So much for the brash and brassy singer with the penchant for life's excesses—she was so squeaky-clean it was an effort to drink the whisky! Adam would never believe it. But then he wasn't likely to believe anything good about her, she realised with a sudden profound pang of sorrow. He'd created a picture in his own mind of what she was like, and it was obvious nothing was going to alter that.

Throwing down the last of the whisky with a shudder, she switched off the bedside lamp and burrowed down beneath the covers, already aware that the alcohol was having an effect, sending tentacles of warmth through her veins. Within minutes she was asleep, her heavy mane of hair spread over the white pillows. Probably because he'd been so much on her mind, she instantly fell into dreaming of Adam, his dark fathomless eyes and granite features dominating her sleep. Turning over, she murmured his name, unconscious of the longing in her voice.

Suddenly she was catapulted violently back to con-

sciousness by rough hands on her shoulder, shaking
her into unwilling life.

'What the. . .?' She glared up at the man who had
been invading her dreams, for a second not even sure
if she was awake or asleep. Adam's face was mere
inches from her own, his eyes hot with a fury she had
never witnessed in him before. She sat up, sweeping
her tumbling hair back from her face with one hand,
then grabbed the covers about her, suddenly aware
that her nightdress was slipping off one shoulder. 'What
are you doing here?' she demanded.

'Never mind that,' he gritted out, the muscles in his
cheeks taut. 'Just what have you been taking, Aurora?'

'Taking?' Thoroughly confused, she stared back at
him, thrown completely off balance by his unexpected
appearance in her bedroom. 'I don't know what you
mean.'

'Don't you?' Grimly he thrust the empty aspirin
bottle beneath her nose. 'Then what's this? I found it
in the kitchen—empty. Then I found you, in bed,
completely unconscious and very hard to waken.'

Despite herself, and probably because she was still
feeling the effects of the whisky she'd taken before
going to bed, Rory began to giggle.

'There's nothing funny about this,' Adam said
harshly. 'Come on, you're going to walk it off.'

'There's nothing to walk off!' But even as she
protested, he gripped her upper arm and began hauling
her unceremoniously from the bed. 'Adam, for goodness' sake! You're crazy—I haven't taken anything.'
She tried to resist, but as she struggled against him, the
ridiculously scanty nightdress threatened to fall off her
shoulders altogether, and embarrassment at her own
state of undress forced her to make a grab for the

material. With his usual lightning-swift reactions he took advantage of the moment to pull her from the bed, and as she stumbled against him, his arms tightened about her involuntarily. The feeling of being pressed against his solid, rock-hard body almost undid her completely, and for a moment she was forced to simply lean against him, her legs all but giving way beneath her.

'You stupid little idiot!' He gripped her upper arms, his fingers pressing cruelly into her tender flesh as he shoved her none too gently away to arm's length. 'You've been drinking as well—are you trying to kill yourself?'

'Now look!' Horribly aware of her own dishevelled state, her tousled hair tumbling about her flushed cheeks, Rory pulled herself up to her full height, summoning up all the strength she possessed to glare regally back at him. 'I haven't the faintest idea what you're trying to imply—but if you don't get out of here in two seconds flat, I'm calling the police. How dare you break into my house and assault me like this?'

His eyes glittered dangerously. 'I'll do a lot more than that if you don't do as you're told. Get walking!' Still gripping her arm, he pushed her ahead of him and she stumbled into a walk, unable to fight his vastly superior strength. 'Now I understand your sudden attack of so-called "flu" back at the nightclub,' he said viciously. 'You were suffering withdrawal symptoms, weren't you, Aurora? And that's why you had to rush back here—alone. You needed a fix. What are you taking?'

Amazement and fury combined in a sudden rush and she stopped dead in her tracks, whirling round on him.

'Are you out of your mind?' Her almond-shaped

eyes wide with incredulity, she stared at him in horror.
'We've been through all this already—I've never taken
drugs in my life!'

'The empty bottle in the kitchen would seem to
contradict that.'

'Aspirin—the bottle held aspirin!' she all but yelled
the words back at him. 'Didn't you read the label?'

'Labels mean nothing,' he shot back. 'You could
have had anything in that bottle.'

'Well, I damn well didn't! The truth is I had nothing
at all in the bottle—it was empty because I'd forgotten
to get new supplies. That's how hooked I am on drugs,
Adam Burns—though why the hell I should even find
it necessary to explain all that to you, I don't know.'

'I've heard the lies of drug abusers before,' he said
implacably. 'I know the lengths they'll go to to cover
up the truth.'

'But you said you believed me! When you tackled
me about it before, you said you believed me.' Rory
gazed helplessly at him through haunted, agonised
eyes. Frustration at his inexplicable change of heart
now had her almost at screaming pitch.

'Even I can be wrong,' he said implacably.

'But why would I agree to help you investigate the
club if I were a user myself?'

'Perhaps because you could be of more use to the
ringleaders that way,' he returned instantly. 'Maybe
you're passing on information to them.'

She shook her head, stunned by the whole incredible
scenario. How could he possibly think such a thing
about her—that she would not only take drugs herself,
but that she'd willingly put him in horrific danger by
acting as a kind of double agent? The whole thing
beggared belief. Suddenly all the fight drained out of

her, leaving her weary and spent. What a mess! What a huge, terrible mess. She was in love with a man who considered her to be lower than the lowest form of human life, yet even that wasn't enough to change her feelings for him. Even now as she looked into those harsh, compelling features, she knew only a terrible longing to simply throw herself into his arms, to find the sanctuary and warmth only he could give her.

'Why did you come here tonight, Adam?' she asked, her voice hollow and strained.

'Because I was worried about you,' he returned drily. 'You looked like death when you left the club. When I arrived, I hammered on your door for several minutes and got no response whatsoever. But you'd left your kitchen window open, so I climbed in through that.'

She gave a single nod. 'OK. So now you've reassured yourself that I'm not at death's door, I'd like you to leave.'

'No.'

Her head shot up. 'What?'

'You heard me. I'm not leaving your side tonight, Aurora—in fact, you may as well get accustomed to having me around, because until this investigation's over, I'm going to be glued to your side like a shadow.'

'You can't be serious!' She could only whisper the words.

Adam nodded grimly. 'Never more serious in my life.'

'I won't allow it! I'll have you arrested for harassing me.'

'You can try,' he shrugged.

She hung her head, weighed down by the enormity of it all, swamped by the prospect of having Adam constantly at her side. The strain of having him in the club practically all the time had been hard enough. She'd never get through the ordeal without cracking up completely. But she knew Adam well enough by now to know he wouldn't make empty threats. She had no choice.

'Very well,' she said at last, 'I'll go along with this crazy scheme—only because it's the only way I can hope to convince you that you're wrong, totally wrong. But I want you to know I'm going to hate every second of having you with me.'

A sardonic smile touched his lips. 'It's entirely mutual, Aurora. Now—find me a blanket.'

She gave him a pained look. 'You can sleep in the spare room. There's a bed already made up in there.'

He shook his head. 'I'll take the chair in your room. I meant what I said, Aurora—I'm going to be your shadow.'

'For how long?' She could barely get the words past lips grown strangely dry.

'For however long it takes.'

CHAPTER NINE

'ADAM'S moved in with you?' Candy made no attempt to hide her astonishment. 'Well, I've got to hand it to you, kiddo—you've still got the capability to amaze me.'

'In what way?' asked Rory.

'I always thought it would be marriage or nothing for you—especially after the way you've kept men at arm's length over the years I've known you.'

Afraid that Candy's probing blue eyes would be able to read far too much in her own features, Rory kept her face averted, taking great pains to straighten a bottle in the already immaculate display in the club's main bar.

'Adam's not the marrying kind,' she said at last.

'But you are,' Candy returned swiftly. She handed over another bottle, frowning thoughtfully. 'Are you happy with this?'

Unthinkingly Rory glanced up. 'Happy?' she echoed. 'Well, of course I'm happy!'

'Then why do you look like a child who's lost its puppy dog?' Candy's eyes narrowed. 'Frankly, Rory, you don't have the look of a woman in love. At least,' she corrected herself, 'not of a woman who's happy in love. You look. . .' she paused consideringly as Rory squirmed beneath her scrutiny '. . .bruised. Not physically bruised, but emotionally.'

Rory made an attempt at a light laugh. 'This love stuff ain't easy.'

'So you are in love with him?' Candy pounced instantly.

Rory sighed. She'd been dreading this. She'd known Candy for too long to have any hope that she would escape without an inquisition. She would never have told her about Adam staying at the farmhouse at all through choice, but Candy was a regular visitor. Sooner or later she would have found out for herself, and the interrogation would have been worse still if she'd thought Rory was trying to keep her in the dark about such a momentous event in her life.

In truth she had done remarkably well staying out of her clutches for the past three days, but then, she reflected ruefully, Adam had kept his promise, staying practically glued to her side. Even now he was just a short distance away, in the club's office, while she supervised the stocking of a new promotional lager in the bar.

'Would I be living with him if I weren't?' she asked.

'I don't know.' Candy eyed her shrewdly. 'You tell me. I'm still getting over the shock of discovering you're living together at all.'

Rory shrugged. 'It's the modern thing to do, isn't it? I'm hardly setting a precedent.'

'True. But in many ways you've always been a very old-fashioned girl. And I don't think this set-up really suits you. I think you're simply going along with what he wants, and frankly that's out of character.'

'You reckon?' Rory returned lightly.

'Yes.' Candy gave a single decisive nod. 'Lions don't generally allow themselves to be dictated to.'

But then lions weren't generally subjected to the kinds of pressures she was under, Rory thought wryly, knowing she could never say the words aloud. If Candy realised the game Adam was playing, she would go storming in with all guns blazing, never stopping to think of the possible consequences, all her protective instincts roused in defence of her best friend.

'Perhaps love changes people's characters,' she suggested with a flippancy she was far from feeling.

'It hasn't changed his,' Candy retorted. 'If anything it's magnified it. Scorpios are supposed to be possessive, but Adam's been acting more like a gaoler recently—he hardly allows you out of his sight. I'm amazed you've managed to shake him off your heels just now.'

Rory smiled wanly, knowing she couldn't deny the accusation. Ever since he'd turned up in her bedroom several nights before, he really had become her shadow, staying constantly by her side. And the worst part of it all was that having him there all the time hadn't lessened her longing for him by one tiny jot. Oh, sometimes it was irritating, even downright infuriating to look round and see him just a couple of paces away, but she only had to look into those dark eyes to feel that treacherous quiver of desire deep in the pit of her stomach.

He'd been a gentleman, she couldn't fault him on that. Even though he'd slept in her bedroom every night, perched uncomfortably on two chairs, he had made no move to seduce her—even to approach her. She should be grateful for that, she told herself irritably—instead, it only served to heighten her growing frustration all the more. Or perhaps he wasn't being considerate, she suddenly realised with a pang—perhaps he hadn't made a move simply because he wasn't in the least attracted to her. After all, she was the one who fell apart at the seams every time they touched, while he remained infuriatingly unmoved.

'He's making a few phone calls,' she said at last. 'I managed to convince him I had work to do. Speaking of which. . .' she gave the other woman a pointed look.

'That's another thing,' Candy continued, far too old a hand at the game to be distracted by such a blatant bid to change the subject, 'I've seen him deep in conversation with quite a few people in the club recently.'

'There's nothing strange about that,' Rory shot back. 'He's a friendly person.'

Candy raised one eyebrow. 'About as friendly as your average Scorpion,' she said wryly. 'Darling girl, have you lost your marbles entirely? Granted, being in love may have addled your brain, but Adam—friendly? Give me a break!'

Despite herself, Rory couldn't help but grin. 'OK, so he's not the most sociable being in the world. Maybe he's trying to change—for my sake.'

'And maybe pigs can fly. Look, I know something's going on here—and I want to get to the bottom of it.'

Rory flinched. This was exactly what she had been afraid of—flibbertigibbet though she was in most things, Candy could be positively terrier-like if she got her teeth into a mystery, refusing to let go until she'd solved everything to her satisfaction. Persuading her that nothing was going on could turn out to be a Herculean task.

'You're imagining things,' she said now with a nonchalant shrug.

'Sure.' Candy's returning glance was worryingly unconvinced. 'OK. You want to work—let's work. What exactly is the plan for this promotions night?'

Rory felt a faint but definite niggle of alarm in the pit of her stomach. This was a new tactic, one she wasn't familiar with. Never in the history of their friendship had Candy given up so easily—and she didn't believe for one split second she had now. She must have decided to get her information some other way—but the only other way was through Adam.

'Candy. . .' she began tentatively.

'The bar looks great. You're doing a terrific job.'

With a faintly fatalistic feeling, Rory glanced up to see Adam approaching the bar. It was as if he'd known—as if he'd somehow been alerted to the fact that she was about to cave in, to spill the beans on their bogus relationship. His expression was as inscrutable as ever, yet she was sure she could detect a warning gleam in his dark eyes. For a second she knew an intense longing to flee—to get a million miles away from this place and everyone in it. Between them, Candy and Adam had hounded her into a corner; she felt beleaguered, under attack from all sides. Then she mentally shook herself. She was being ridiculous, letting things get out of proportion. She could cope. At the end of the day, she was still in charge of the club. As to her own life—of that she wasn't quite so sure.

'Hi,' she managed to summon up a smile. 'Made all your calls?'

He nodded. 'Let's get out of here.'

Riled by the peremptory note of command in his voice, Rory opened her mouth to give him a scathing reply, but just in time caught the sideways glance slid her way by Candy and bit her tongue. The other woman was already sceptical—she couldn't afford to add more fuel to the fire of her suspicions by biting Adam's head off the way she'd simply love to do. But damn him—it was bad enough that he be high-handed and autocratic when they were alone together—did he really have to carry it into the public arena too?

She turned to Candy with an apologetic grimace. 'Can you finish up here?' she asked.

Candy nodded slowly. 'Sure thing. Go and take some time off. Take advantage of the fact that the club's shut tonight. You deserve a break.'

They were barely out of the club before Rory turned on Adam, no longer able to keep the lid on her simmering anger.

'How dare you order me about in front of my friend?' she demanded. 'Just who do you think you are?'

He was clearly unmoved by her outburst. 'I'm supposed to be the man you're deeply in love with, remember?'

'Remember? How could I possibly forget, when you're there beside me at every single turn?'

A slight smile played about his lips. 'Getting to you, is it, Aurora?' he queried softly. 'What's the matter—am I cramping your style? Getting in the way of things you'd rather be doing?'

She shot him a disgusted look. 'If you mean drugs, then no, Adam, you're way off line and you have been all the time—as you'd realise for yourself if you'd just open your eyes and see the truth instead of what you want to see.'

To her astonishment he stopped abruptly in his tracks, his hand snaking out to grasp her wrist and whirl her back to face him.

'What I want to see?' he echoed. 'You really think I want to see a stunningly beautiful woman strung out on drugs?' Slowly he shook his head. 'You're the one who's way off line.' He lifted his hand to her face, tracing the line of her cheekbones with one exquisitely gentle finger, and she quivered helplessly beneath his touch. 'What I want to see is the woman you should be—the one you were born to be. Perfect, uncontaminated, uncorrupted by the evil this imperfect world has to offer.'

To her horror Rory felt the sting of tears behind her eyes and looked away helplessly. Just what was it about this man that he could arouse her strongest emotions so very easily? she thought hazily. She'd never been the crying sort—but it just took a few well-chosen words from him to reduce her to a jelly.

'I'm far from perfect,' she said now in a low, husky voice. 'But I'm not the fool you believe me to be either. Maybe one day you'll realise that.' Pulling herself together with a visible effort, she managed to glare at him. 'And don't change the subject. Ordering me about in front of Candy, knowing I had no choice other than to meekly obey, was downright contemptible!'

'How long has Candy known you?' he asked abruptly.

She frowned, thrown by the apparent change of tack.

'Years. We were friends at school, then I took her on as my personal assistant when my singing career began to take off. Why?'

'Would you say she knows you better than anyone else?'

Rory nodded. 'Better than another living soul.'

'If I were to treat you like Dresden china, placing you on a pedestal and worshipping at your feet, would she believe you were in love with me?'

Despite herself, Rory couldn't help but give a little laugh.

'No.'

He gave a single, satisfied nod. 'No. Because she knows you to be a strong character. She also knows you need someone even stronger as a partner. Someone who can bring you to heel when you need it. You'd never respect anyone weak, let alone fall in love with them.'

'That doesn't give you the right to dictate to me.'

'I think it does.'

She shrugged her shoulders, temporarily giving up the fight. Once again they'd reached an impasse, but in truth it really didn't matter. As terrible as these times were, they were only temporary. Eventually Adam would disappear from her life, and she'd probably never see him again, certainly would never have to fight with him again. She only wished she could look forward to that day—instead, she realised, aching inside at the prospect, she was dreading it. Life without Adam would return quickly to normal, but it would be so empty.

'Where are we going?' she asked in a hollow little voice.

'Candy's right,' he returned, 'you do need a break.' Unaccountably his features softened for a fleeting second. 'You've been under a lot of pressure recently. We're going for a walk.'

'A walk?' She couldn't have been more surprised if he'd suggested hang-gliding from the top of the nearest skyscraper. 'Where?'

'Out in the country.' A faintly mocking grin touched his lips. 'Your lungs have been subjected to an intense diet of nightclub smoke and decorating fumes—you could do with some fresh air. And I know just the place to get it.'

*   *   *

Rory drew in a deep breath, letting her lungs fill with the cool pine-scented air of the forest, then threw her head back as she exhaled, her hair tumbling over her shoulders in shining, rippling waves. For the first time in days she felt relaxed, rejuvenated even, as though the trees had somehow managed to impart new life into her.

'You were right.' Unable to keep a smile of pure pleasure from her lips, she glanced at the man at her side. 'This place is terrific. How did you find it?'

'I've known this forest for years,' Adam returned easily. 'I used to come here as a kid with my parents.'

'You did?' It was hard to imagine this tall, powerfully built man as a young, unformed boy. 'Were you an only child?'

He shook his head. 'I had a sister, younger than me.'

His dark eyes were shuttered, his features more harshly etched than ever. All the signs were there, clearly telling her to back off, but suddenly she was tired of treading warily round this enigmatic character. It came to her now just how little she knew about him—much less than he knew about her life, which was to a great extent an open book, despite his determination to believe she had a dark side.

'You had a sister?' she said softly. 'What happened to her?'

'She died.' His voice was flat, unemotional, yet she heard the wealth of anguish behind the stark words.

'How?' She was walking unarmed into dangerous territory, but something deep inside was urging her on, refusing to let her back off now. 'How did she die, Adam?'

He stopped walking, staring straight ahead of him into the forest. 'She took an overdose.'

Pain sliced into her like a sharp knife, making her close her eyes helplessly. Everything made sense now—his obsessional hatred of the drugs world, his grim determination to fight the dealers, his refusal to accept her repeated protests that she had never been involved. She'd inwardly fumed when he told her drug users were habitual liars, that they'd say or do anything to get what they wanted. But he had been there—he had watched someone he loved being drawn deeper and deeper into the morass. She could see it in his face, his guard, for the first time since she'd known him, completely lowered.

'Tell me about her, Adam,' she urged gently.

For a moment she thought he would refuse, then he shrugged. 'What is there to tell? Lisa was young, beautiful and easily led.'

His words were almost dismissive, but this time Rory wasn't fooled. Intuitively she felt the depths of the anguish he'd suffered, knew without having to be told how hard he had struggled to help his sister, understood how devastating it must have been for him to realise she'd gone beyond his help. Unthinkingly she reached out to him, placing a gentle hand on his face, feeling the muscles of his cheek tense beneath her fingers.

'I'm so sorry, Adam,' she whispered, forgetting everything else in that moment but the need to comfort a troubled fellow human being. He moved his head slightly and she sighed softly. She should have known he would reject her sympathy. Then her eyes widened in surprise as she felt his lips against her fingers, his unexpected caress sending shooting stars through her veins.

For a long moment all she could do was stare back

at him, his dark fathomless eyes holding her in thrall. She never knew which one of them made the first move, but suddenly, unaccountably, she was in his arms, his hands pressing against her back to draw her closer still. She tried to murmur his name, but the soft sound became a groan as his mouth closed over hers and she was lost. Heaven knew, it had been difficult enough to remain even slightly detached when they had been putting on an act for the benefit of an audience. Now, with only the trees and the birds of the forest to see them, she was helpless against the waves of longing pounding through her like a restless ocean.

Ravenous for more, she opened her mouth to him, greedily welcoming the invasion of his tongue, her hands tangling in his dark hair. A tiny remote voice in her brain told her she was crazy, that this whole thing was crazy, but it was instantly silenced, reason standing no chance against the far stronger forces of sheer need.

His hands swept restlessly over her body, touching, stroking, his fingers igniting fires wherever they roamed. She arched up against him as he found his way unerringly beneath her light sweatshirt to her naked breasts, her breath quickening as his thumbs grazed her nipples, making them pucker into hard little buds.

She lost all sense of time, all awareness of place, conscious only of him—the taste of him, the feel of him beneath her hands, the gloriously masculine smell of him. Nothing in the world seemed important any more, the only reality his hard body pressed against her own. Driven beyond sense, she made no protest when he scooped her easily into his arms and strode deeper into the forest. Well away from the beaten track he laid her gently on a bed of moss and bracken, and she opened her arms to him, loath to lose his touch for even a second.

'Dear God, Rory,' he murmured, 'you're driving me out of my mind!'

'Good.' Her voice, husky and breathless, held an exultant note. This was what it was all about, she realised hazily—this was what her whole life had been leading up to, this man, this place, this almost unbearably exquisite time out of time.

He shrugged out of his jacket and her hands went to his cotton shirt, fumbling in their haste to undo the buttons. At last they were all free and she pushed the material impatiently aside, her fingers losing themselves in the gloriously thick mat of dark curling hair on his powerful chest.

'Are you sure this is what you want, Rory?' The words murmured through her hair and she nodded, barely able to speak. She'd never wanted anything more in her life—but it was more than just a physical need, much much more. Everything within her was reaching out to him—to be denied now would be a torture more than she could bear.

The forest air was cool on her naked limbs as Adam stripped away the last of her clothes and she was aware of a glorious feeling of freedom, totally devoid of embarrassment, as he gazed at her, his eyes sweeping boldly over her body, drinking their fill.

'You're like a dryad,' he told her, 'or a beautiful wild animal. A golden-limbed lioness in human form.'

And you are the scorpion with a fatal sting. The words echoed like a warning bell in her mind, but she was helpless to heed them as his dark head bent over her, his mouth warm against one nipple, the gentle tug of his lips sending curling fingers of desire deep into the pit of her stomach. His hand moved with agonising slowness over the silken skin of her thigh and the breath caught in her throat, everything within her willing his hand to move closer and closer still to the very centre of her need for him. When at last he touched her there, all the longing pent-up within her released itself in a single hoarse cry, and she thrust her fingers into his hair, pulling his head back to hers, her lips parting in an invitation that needed no words.

Then he moved, and the hard strength of him dissolved the very bones within her as she lay dazzled beneath the forest sky. Bracken scratched her tender skin, but she was barely aware of it, her every nerve ending alive only to the man touching her with such consummate skill. He looked into her face and she smiled.

'Make love to me,' she whispered, answering the unspoken question in his eyes. 'I need you to.'

Then there was no more need for words as he slid deep within her, conquering the unchartered territories of her body and of her soul with one powerful thrust. Her fingers dug deep into his shoulders as she clung to him, caught up in a maelstrom of sensation, too stunned by the sheer beauty of it all to register more than the most fleeting second of pain. She was whirling higher and higher, her body finding for itself a rhythm it had never been taught, till unknowingly she cried his name aloud, unable to contain the feelings building to explosion point a second longer.

Reality returned slowly as she lay with eyes closed, still savouring the feel of the warm and powerful body lying on top of her own. With a soft sigh she buried her face in his shoulder, wishing she could simply stay there forever, warm, cocooned, protected from the outside

world. But at last she looked up at him, a soft con-
tented smile playing about her lips. The smile froze as
she saw the dark, forbidding look in his eys. Dear
heaven, what now? How could he possibly look at her
like that after the beauty they'd just shared together?

'Adam?' she ventured tentatively.

He shook his head abruptly as though to ward off
whatever she might be about to say.

'Put your clothes on, Aurora,' he said. 'You feel
cold.'

That was probably true, she realised, scrambling
away from him to reach for her discarded clothes. A
few moments ago she had been burning up in his arms,
caught up in the fever of his lovemaking, but now the
blood seemed to have turned to ice in her veins, frozen
by his uncaring tones. How could he? How could he
hold her so tenderly one moment, only to treat her like
this the next? Misery gripped her heart like a vice.
She'd been a fool, a stupid crazy fool, too blinded by
love to see that she was being used, too mesmerised by
longing to realise Adam wanted only her body. He had
always believed her to be promiscuous—now he was
probably convinced, she thought bitterly, her face
flaming as she recalled her total abandon in his arms.
It needed all the pride she possessed to turn to him a
moment later, ashen-faced but in control.

'Will you take me home now, please,' she said
stiltedly. 'I've had enough of the forest for one day.'

CHAPTER TEN

THEY drove back to the farmhouse in total silence, Rory too confused and unhappy to utter a single word, knowing too well that if she did, the floodgates on her feelings would open, releasing a veritable tidal wave. As usual it was impossible to tell from Adam's granite features just how he was feeling—if he was feeling anything at all, she thought savagely. That afternoon, hearing him talk about his sister, then lying beneath the trees with him, she had really thought she had finally broken through to a real live human being beneath the glacial exterior. Now the barriers were back in place, as solid and secure as though they had never been breached at all.

As they drove into the courtyard, she glanced at him in surprise as he kept the car engine running.

'I won't stay tonight,' he said shortly. 'I think we both need some time to be alone.'

Rory should have been relieved. Instead all she could feel was pain. So now he couldn't even bear to be with her. Well, what had she expected? Protestations of undying love?

'Aren't you afraid I'll dive straight into the drugs stash I've been hoarding?' Biting her lip, she looked away from his dark, probing eyes, hating the obvious bitterness in her own voice. Why couldn't she maintain a cool front too?

'Only if you're a bigger fool than I take you for.'

Unable to take any more, she slammed the car door

and headed for the farmhouse without a backward glance, managing with an effort to keep her head high. In the kitchen, as she heard the sound of the car driving away, she slumped on to a stool, her long hair spilling over her fingers as she dropped her head into her hands with a heavy groan. What now—what was she supposed to do now? All her life she had had a clear vision of who she was and where she was going. That had all changed with the arrival in her life of Adam Burns. Thanks to him, she was like a boat without a rudder, drifting aimlessly in a river, letting its currents take her wherever they wanted.

'Some lioness you're turning out to be,' she muttered, with grim humour. 'More like a spineless jellyfish!'

For a long time she sat at the breakfast bar, gazing into space, searching for answers and finding none. At last, with a sigh, she got to her feet and wandered upstairs to the bathroom. Maybe a long soothing bath would help put the world back on its proper axis, though frankly she doubted it. Sliding into the scented water, she laid her head back against the cool surface of the bath, willing the heat to relax her tired and knotted muscles. Right now she'd like nothing better than to climb into bed and stay there for a week, sleeping her troubles away.

If only things could be resolved that easily! Pursing her lips ruefully, she shook her head. That had been the crux of the problem the whole way through—she had been too passive, allowing Adam to call the shots with no more than a token protest. And where had it got her? Exactly nowhere. Well, it couldn't be allowed to continue. She had to get her hands back on the reins, had to re-establish at least a degree of control over her own life. Not relishing the prospect in the slightest, she slid right under the water for a long moment, as though seeking sanctuary, then sat up abruptly, creating a tidal wave. And it was about time she started making a few waves, she told herself firmly. Starting with Adam.

A couple of hours later she glanced at herself in a mirror and gave a rueful little chuckle. She hadn't planned it deliberately, but she even looked as if she were heading into battle, clad in a flying suit, flat boots and a bomber jacket, her long hair captured in a plait. The confused, anguished look had disappeared from her tawny almond-shaped eyes, replaced by a fiercely determined light. She gave a grimly satisfied nod. If you ignored the shadows beneath her eyes and the paleness of her complexion, she looked like her old self again.

'Adam,' she pledged quietly, 'you'll never know what hit you.'

It was fortunate that they'd both driven back to the farmhouse after leaving the nightclub, before carrying on to the forest in Adam's car, so her own vehicle was parked outside in the courtyard. Not that she would have allowed a little thing like lack of transport to get in her way—in her current mood she would have hired a private helicopter if necessary to get her to her destination. And that destination was—Adam's place.

'Please don't be out,' she murmured to the empty car as she drove along the quiet country roads. She'd managed to psych herself into just the proper frame of mind for a confrontation, but there was no guarantee that it would last. She'd never been to Adam's, but she knew he was renting a small cottage just a few miles away from her own home. He had even pointed it out to her one day, although as she recalled now, he hadn't actually invited her to stop by.

'Tough,' she said aloud. 'For once in your life, Adam, you're going to go along with what someone else wants. Namely—me.'

Seeing his car parked outside his cottage brought both relief and a fresh rush of nerves, in more or less equal measure. Then she frowned, spotting a second, unfamiliar vehicle. If he was entertaining visitors, he might not be at all pleased to have her arriving uninvited on the doorstep. Maybe she should postpone the whole crazy idea—or better still, drop it altogether. Annoyed at her own uncharacteristic weakness, she clenched her hands into fists, willing a return of the earlier combative mood.

Remembering the old adage that forewarned was forearmed, she parked her car just out of sight of the cottage down a little side lane. Right now she felt the need of every weapon in the armoury, including surprise. Smiling a little ruefully at her own foolishness, she walked down the lane, guessing rightly that it would take her to the back of the cottage. But as she reached the back door, the sound of a loud, angry voice stopped her in her tracks. It wasn't Adam.

'So come on, Mr Burns,' the voice said sneeringly, 'what gives? Just what is this little cat-and-mouse game you've been playing?'

'No game,' she heard Adam's voice, as cool and calm as ever. 'I wanted to meet you to arrange a deal.'

The other man gave a harsh bark of laughter. 'You think I arrived in the last shower or rain? I can recognise a set-up when I see one, and you, Mr Burns, have been trying to set me up. I can thank the lovely lady from the nightclub for putting me wise to that one!'

The blood ran cold in Rory's veins as she stood rooted to the spot in horror. What lovely lady? What deal?

'I don't know what you're talking about,' Adam returned with an apparent total lack of concern. 'Your front-of-house boys don't have the authority to deal in the kind of quantities I'm interested in. You do.' He paused. 'At least, I assume you do, otherwise I'm wasting my time.'

The man growled angrily. 'If you think I'm falling into that trap you really have picked the wrong man to tangle with. I'm on to you, Burns, and I'm going to put an end to your little game—once and for all!'

Rory stood on the back doorstep, gripped by a moment of rare indecision. What on earth was she supposed to do? Adam was obviously in trouble, but a wrong move on her part could make things a hundred times worse. Then she mentally shook herself—standing around on this doorstep certainly wasn't going to help. But the first thing she had to do was suss out the lie of the land—there was no point in going charging in with all guns blazing.

Her heart in her mouth, she dropped to her knees and crawled along the path till she reached the window looking into what she guessed must be the front room of the cottage. She didn't dare raise her head to look through the window in case she was spotted, but at least from here she could make a fair guess at where Adam and the stranger were located in the room. From the sounds of their voices it was obvious they were both somewhere near the centre, she decided.

She crawled back to the door and got to her feet,

taking a deep steadying breath as she reached for the handle, grimacing slightly as she eased it open and stepped through the doorway, sending up a silent prayer that no creaking floorboard would announce her presence prematurely. God was clearly on her side and she made it to the living-room door without a hitch. But now what? She gave a wry little grin, realising she had no real plan of action in mind. Her only thought was to help Adam. Well, she'd simply have to depend on luck to get her through. Luck—and the element of surprise, since neither man knew she was there.

If she was going to catch Adam's uninvited guest completely off guard, she'd have to do something suitably dramatic, and the thought sent a rush of adrenalin pounding through her blood, mixing giddyingly with the nerves already churning in the pit of her stomach. It was now or never. Hearing the stranger's voice become louder and angrier still, she raised one long booted leg and aimed an almighty kick at the door. She knew a quick surge of satisfaction when the door flew open, but there was no time to revel in pride at her own achievement as she took in the scene beyond the door.

'What the hell!' A tall, powerfully built man leapt to his feet, his features twisted in a mixture of surprise and fury. He made a lunge towards Rory, but Adam proved too fast for him, grabbing him from behind in a tackle that would have felled an ox.

'Watch out, Rory!' Adam's warning yell came almost too late as she in turn was grabbed. She knew an instant's anger at her own lack of foresight—she should have known Adam's inquisitor wouldn't be alone—then all the training she'd undergone in self-defence took over and she jabbed both elbows savagely backward, hearing her attacker give a pained grunt as his grip on her loosened. It was only a momentary lapse on his part, but it gave her enough time to whirl round on him, her eyes widening as she spotted a revolver in his hand. But even as he lifted it, reflexes that she'd always prayed would be lightning-fast in a showdown proved their sterling worth, galvanising her into action. She lifted her right arm and brought it down in a slashing sideways sweep on to his wrist, sending the gun clattering harmlessly to the corner of the room. They both made a dive for it, but Rory's litheness and agility won the day over bulk and sheer brute strength, and she hit the ground at a roll, grabbing the revolver and jumping to her feet again in one graceful, almost balletic movement.

'Now,' pointing the gun towards her attacker and praying inwardly she wouldn't be called upon to use it since she hadn't the faintest idea how firearms worked, she glanced over towards Adam and the other man still engaged in a tussle on the floor, 'I suggest we call a halt to all this nonsense.'

'Give me the gun, bitch!' the second man snarled, his coarse, ugly features contorted with rage. She stared disdainfully back at him, her eyes narrowing contemptuously.

'I don't believe you're in any position to go calling anyone names,' she returned, affecting a calmness she was in reality a million miles from feeling. 'Adam, if you'd be good enough to finish what you're doing, perhaps you could take this weapon from me, since I'm sure you're more accustomed to guns than I am.' A maliciously playful smile curved her lips as she aimed the revolver at her attacker's mid-section. 'After all, I'd hate it to go off by accident.'

Giving his sparring partner one last crack on the jaw which effectively put him out of the reckoning, Adam rose to his feet, and took the gun from her suddenly nerveless fingers.

'What the hell are you doing here?' he muttered through gritted teeth.

'Nice to see you too, darling,' she drawled in reply. 'And of course you're quite welcome—any time you need to be saved from thugs, just give me a call.'

'Never mind all that now,' he shot back impatiently. 'Are you any good at tying knots?'

'I wasn't a Girl Guide for nothing. Just give me the rope.'

He jerked his head towards the door. 'In the hall cupboard, beneath the stairs. But first. . .' she paused in mid-stride, looking back enquiringly, 'you'd better put in a call to the police.'

She did as he asked, then fetched the coils of rope, quickly and efficiently trussing the two men like Christmas turkeys as Adam stood over them with the gun. The one who was still conscious snarled and swore as she tightened the rope about his ankles, and she shook her head reprovingly.

'Such language!' she said. 'Didn't your mother ever wash out your mouth with soap and water for cursing?'

'I'll get you for this, bitch!' he spat viciously. 'Just you mind your back in future!'

Rory shrugged. 'I'll endeavour to employ a shade more vigilance than you did,' she returned lightly, then cocked her head to one side as she heard the sound of a siren. 'I do believe I hear our wonderful boys in blue.'

As the car screeched to a halt outside, Adam looked over at her, his dark eyes faintly wondering.

'Well done, Aurora,' he said quietly. 'I've never seen anything as cool in my life.'

'Cool?' She tried to grin back at him, but suddenly, unaccountably, her teeth were chattering and she gave an enormous, involuntary shudder. 'You're the master of cool. I was simply trying to emulate. . .' but whatever she might have said was lost to the word forever as she crumpled bonelessly to the floor in a dead faint.

When she came to she was lying in a strange bed in a strange room, and she sat bolt upright, gripped by panic.

'Hey, hey! It's all right, Rory, you're safe now.'

Her heart still pounding nineteen to the dozen, she looked over towards the window, seeing for the first time a familiar, powerfully-built figure standing there.

'Adam! I thought. . .'

'I know what you thought. But it's all right—they've gone now.' He crossed the room in a couple of strides to sit on the bed beside her. 'They're currently assisting with an inquiry that's been giving the police quite a few headaches for the last few months.' He stroked a wayward curl back from her face and she trembled beneath the unexpected caress. 'You and I are also required to put in an appearance at the police station later, but I managed to persuade them you weren't in a fit state to answer questions right now.' He smiled, and there was real, genuine warmth in his eyes. 'Although when they first walked in and found you out cold on the floor, they thought you were one of the gang too! I had a hard job convincing them otherwise.'

Rory giggled weakly, then lay back against the pillows, suddenly overwhelmed by everything that had happened that day, not least by the totally uncharacter-

istic tenderness in his voice. Maybe the whole thing
had been a dream, she thought hazily—any minute
now she'd wake up to find herself sunbathing on her
own back lawn.

'Are you up to talking?' Adam asked quietly.

'I'm not sure,' she returned guardedly. 'That all
depends on what you want to talk about.'

'Everything.'

She sighed. 'That's what I was afraid of.'

'After what I saw here today, I don't believe you're
afraid of anything.'

How little he knew, she thought ruefully. He had no
idea that she was mortally afraid of the way his
nearness was making her heart pound completely out
of control, no idea that she was having to exert every
ounce of self-control she possessed to stop herself
reaching out to him, no idea of how desperately she
loved him. And he must never know.

Deep down, well hidden beneath the façade of
arrogance and ice that he presented to the world, a
warm, caring heart beat within Adam Burns. Rory had
only seen fleeting glimpses of it, but enough to know it
was there. If he had the slightest suspicion of how she
really felt, it could well bring out the sympathetic side
of his nature. She couldn't bear that, couldn't stand to
see pity in those dark compelling eyes.

'What's a little thing like a revolver between friends?'
she said flippantly. 'All right, Adam, we'll talk, but not
here. Let me get myself together, and we'll convene
the meeting downstairs.' Well away from this bed and
all the thoughts it was putting into her wayward mind.

'Fine,' he returned softly. 'Just come down when
you're ready.'

CHAPTER ELEVEN

'So WHERE do we start?' Flopping inelegantly into a comfortable big armchair, Rory nodded her thanks as Adam handed her a mug of coffee, and took a sip of the hot reviving brew. 'I think perhaps you'd better fill me in on just exactly what's been happening.'

His eyes glinted humorously. 'After what's happened here today, I think perhaps you're right!' He leaned over, bracing both hands on the arms of her chair. 'I haven't thanked you yet.'

'Thanked me?' She blinked up at him, horribly aware that his nearness was having its usual unsettling effect on her blood pressure.

'For coming to my rescue. It was a mad, crazy thing to do, but nevertheless. . .'

She tried to shrug it off. 'You'd probably have managed without me.'

'Perhaps. We'll never know. But I do know I was in the presence of a very dangerous man.'

'The guy with the gun?' she queried.

Adam shook his dark head. 'No. He was just the hired thug. A lot of brawn but very little brain.'

'So who was he—the other man?'

Adam stood upright, taking a few restless paces round the room. 'Bart Conroy—the Boss. The man I've been trying to reach ever since I first started this whole thing.'

'Why?' she queried.

'Why? Because there's never any point in rooting

out just the workers and leaving the management free. A man like that can always replace his front-line troops, so to get only them would have been pointless.'

'But have you "got" him?' Rory's features creased into a frown. 'Before I burst through that door, I'd been listening at the window—I distinctly recall that he was refusing to say anything really damning. He was obviously afraid you were taping the conversation.'

Adam smiled. 'I didn't need to. Several other infinitely more damaging conversations involving him have been taped over the past few weeks. He's been photographed too.'

'He has?' Her eyes widened incredulously. 'How did you manage that?'

'Do you remember the man I was talking to in the club? The sandy-haired one?' She nodded. 'He's one of Bart's henchmen. But unknown to Bart he's also something of a double agent.'

'He's been working for you?'

Adam's expression didn't change. 'Let just say I managed to convince him his hopes of future freedom were rather greater working with me than with Bart.'

Rory shook her head wonderingly. 'You really do like to sail close to the wind, don't you? Why did Bart decide to confront you today?'

'Men like Bart are always suspicious of new clients— and particularly of ones like me who start talking big business, not just trifling little deals. Understandably he kept tabs on me, trying to decide whether I was genuine before agreeing to negotiate with me.'

'Which is why you needed me,' Rory cut in. 'As your cover.'

He nodded, a faint trace of apology in his eyes.

'Correct. I had to make him believe there was a good reason for my being constantly in the club.'

She looked down at her own long denim-clad legs, unconsciously smoothing the material with her fingers.

'I'm glad I was of some use to you,' she said, unable to keep an edge of tartness from her voice. Then a new thought struck her and she glanced up at him again. 'He mentioned a woman in the club—a "lovely lady" who'd put him wise to what you were doing. It wasn't me, Adam!'

His lips quirked at the corners. 'How very immodest of you to assume it was,' he returned mockingly, then shook his head. 'I know it wasn't you, Aurora.'

'Then who?'

'One of the waitresses—Jenna Brown. I've been keeping my eye on her for a while, but it seems she'd been returning the favour without my being aware of it.' He gave a self-deprecating shrug. 'My mind hasn't always been focused on this operation as fully as it should have been.'

The cryptic little comment sparked off a tiny glimmer of hope deep within her—could he be trying to tell her that she'd proved distracting? Rory shook the thought away. It was foolish to allow any kind of hope for the future to take root.

'So you were right all along,' she murmured. 'Well, you've proved your point about me not knowing enough to be a manager. What now?' With a supreme effort, she managed to keep her tone casual, almost indifferent.

'You and I—and quite a few of the nightclub staff—will be required to help the police put all the pieces of the jigsaw together,' said Adam.

'And then you'll be talking to my father about

buying the club.' It was a statement rather than a question.

He shook his head. 'I've grown to realise over the past few weeks just how much the place really does mean to you,' he said quietly. 'It's more than just a nightclub to you. Don't worry, Aurora—I won't be going after it any more.'

She should have felt relief—wasn't this what she'd been longing to hear? Instead she felt the inexplicable sting of tears. 'So you'll be leaving, then?' she said hoarsely.

He nodded, and a shaft of pain more piercing than a sword sliced into her heart. But in truth she couldn't possibly have expected anything else—true to his Scorpio nature, Adam Burns was a loner, he needed to travel light and unencumbered. Even if he'd shown any signs at all of wanting to have her around—which he hadn't—she'd be nothing more than a burden.

Laying down her coffee-cup, she rose to her feet in a lithe, graceful movement that completely belied the heaviness of her spirit.

'Well,' she said lightly, 'if you ever need a partner in battling crime again, you know where to find me. Now, shall we go down to the police station? I'd like to get this whole thing over and done with as quickly as possible. Then perhaps life can finally get back to normal—I hope!'

Over the next few days Rory began to wonder if life would ever return to anything even remotely resembling normal. She seemed to be caught up in a permanent giddying whirl, of trying to run the nightclub, making herself available to the police whenever they needed her, and coping with the demands of a sensation-hungry Press which had swooped on to the drugs-bust story with its famous heroine like a pack of vultures.

'Did you really expect anything else?' Adam asked one afternoon after she'd flung the phone back into its rest, exasperated beyond measure by the persistence of one particular reporter. 'It's a good story. But if you think things are bad now, just wait till the case has been to court. That's when the Press will really start having a field day.'

'It's all very well for you,' she grumbled, sweeping one hand through her already tousled mane of hair. 'You'll doubtless go to ground and leave me to cope with everything.' When he didn't answer, she looked up at him accusingly. 'Unless of course you're intending to disappear even sooner than that.'

'I'll be here for the court case,' he returned calmly.

'But you are going?' she persisted.

He nodded, and she looked away, closing her eyes against the sting of tears.

'Then go now,' she said, the pain she was feeling inside making her voice harsh and raw. 'I don't need you.'

'I know you don't,' Adam said gently. 'You're a strong woman, Aurora.'

'Not the helpless drug addict you once believed me to be?' Terrified he'd realise just how weak she felt right now, she was deliberately goading him.

'I never did believe it,' he assured her.

'You didn't?' His admission took her by surprise. 'But that night you turned up at the farmhouse, you said. . .'

'I was going to stick to you like a shadow.' His smile was self-deprecating. 'Because it suited my purposes to stay close to you. Quite unwittingly you played right into my hands that night, Aurora—I knew you hadn't been taking drugs, but it gave me the perfect excuse for sticking around. By helping me, you were placing yourself in danger. I needed your help, but I had to protect you as well.' His lips twisted wryly. 'I hadn't realised just how well you were able to protect yourself! But I always knew you were fiercely independent and I knew how you'd react to my eternal presence if you realised I was there as a self-appointed bodyguard.' His shoulders lifted fractionally. 'So—I kept up the pretence of believing you were using drugs, hoping you'd accept having me around all the time in a bid to prove your own innocence.'

Rory shook her head, finding it hard to take in all that he was telling her.

'What made you so sure about me?' she queried.

His features seemed to tighten. 'I said it already— you're a strong woman. You've sought and found your own solutions to problems. Drugs are the panacea of the weak.'

'Like Lisa?' She barely whispered the words.

'Like Lisa.' For a long moment he sat in silence, staring unseeingly into space. Then he seemed to reach a decision, his night-dark eyes more compelling than ever as he looked back at her. 'Lisa was a singer too.'

'A singer?' Rory blinked in surprise. Somehow that was the last thing she'd expected to hear. 'Would I have heard of her?'

He smiled grimly. 'No. She was just a young kid fronting a band, determined she was going to make it to the top—like her idol.'

'Who was that?' Even as she said the words, Rory

shuddered, caught in the grip of a sudden, devastating premonition.

'You, Aurora,' he said in a voice that was eerily quiet. 'She tried to emulate you right from the start. She watched every video you ever made, trying to analyse just what it was that made you so special, so different from all the rest.'

'She shouldn't have tried!' Rory cried, feeling the weight of guilt settle on her shoulders like a suffocating cloak, even though she knew in her heart she couldn't be held to blame for this tragedy. 'She should have developed her own style.'

'I tried to tell her that,' he said. 'She was talented, though in a different way, but I could never make her see that.' He was silent for a moment. 'She loved the way you could stride on to any stage with that easy cat-like walk of yours and instantly dominate the place. She loved the way you teased the crowds, made them laugh, made them love you. She wanted the same things. But she couldn't do it.'

'So she turned to drugs.' It was an old, old story. She'd seen the same thing happen to too many others in the music business, not because they'd tried and failed to be carbon copies of Aurora Blake, but simply because they'd tried to force a talent they simply didn't possess. Failure proved too much for them to cope with, and they sought comfort in false succour.

She shook her head sadly. No wonder Adam had seemed at times to hate her, certainly to despise her. He blamed her for the death of his sister. And that put the biggest barrier of all between them. Even though it wasn't her fault, she could never hope to overcome something that immense.

'That's really what drew me here in the first place,'

he said quietly. 'I wanted to find out what you were really like behind the rock-star image. I wanted to know if Lisa's idol had feet of clay.' His dark eyes regarded her steadily. 'For the sake of her memory I wouldn't have hesitated to bring you crashing down from that pedestal if I'd discovered anything damning about you.' He shook his head, the glimmer of a smile playing about his mouth. 'But I didn't. Lisa chose well. The tragedy of her life was that she couldn't accept that she'd never be you.'

Rory felt a sadness more poignant and piercing than anything she'd ever known. 'Please leave now, Adam,' she said steadily, pride alone preventing her breaking heart from showing in her voice.

He seemed to hesitate, but perhaps something in her face persuaded him not to protest. 'Will you be all right, Rory?'

Hearing the pet name he had used so seldom nearly caved her in completely, but she looked up at him with a bright smile.

'Sure I will.'

He gave a slight nod. 'Then I'll see you in court.'

'I'll keep a seat for you.'

Her smile survived almost intact until the door closed behind him. Then she dropped her face into her hands, unable to stem the flood of tears a second longer.

CHAPTER TWELVE

SEVEN DAYS. Just seven days since he'd gone, and each one had seemed like an eternity. They should have passed quickly—heaven knew she'd had more than enough to keep her occupied. Outwardly she had seemed no different—she'd laughed and joked with the customers, dealt with any business matters competently and efficiently, managed to get things back on to an even keel at the club. In reality, though, she'd felt like one of the walking wounded.

She knew from the frequent worried glances the other woman sent in her direction that Candy had seen through the act, but she'd managed with some effort to avoid her, always finding some pretext to disappear in the opposite direction whenever Candy appeared on the horizon. In her present fragile state, an inquisition, no matter how well-intentioned, would have shattered her into a million pieces.

And today was the big day—the day of the children's party. The day when the nation's number one heart-throb Ace Elliot would descend on the club like a god from Olympus, no doubt surrounded by adoring minions and yet more reporters. How ironic now to think that she'd planned the event partly to prove she was capable of organising something major—to show Adam she could pull off a real coup. None of that mattered now. He'd gone, and the club was still hers. Without him in the frame as a serious bidder she had no real fears that her father would decide to sell.

With a heavy sigh Rory levered herself out of bed, her movements jerky and uncoordinated, completely lacking the unconscious grace she'd always possessed. As soon as she reached the club, as soon as she was back in the public eye, she would have to switch on the false persona that had carried her through the past week. But for now, alone in the farmhouse, there was no need for pretence.

Moving like an automaton, she went through all the motions of washing, dressing and putting on make-up. Frankly she'd rather have dragged on comfortable old jeans and a sweatshirt, but she knew the children would expect the Aurora Blake they'd seen on television, and she couldn't disappoint them. Her appetite had apparently disappeared through the door with Adam, but she forced herself to eat breakfast, knowing she had a long and probably arduous day to get through.

That was probably the understatement of the decade, she acknowledged ruefully some hours later, as she grabbed the first opportunity of the entire afternoon to simply stop moving and stand still in one place for longer than ten seconds. These creatures weren't children—they were whirling dervishes! And though she was certain she'd only sent out a couple of hundred invitations, it felt as though there must be at least ten times as many of the little darlings present.

Still—she couldn't help but give a little chuckle as she watched one small boy in calipers crossing the dance floor at an amazingly fast clip, hotly pursued by a red-faced Candy—the children had somehow managed to drag her out of the fog of misery that had enveloped her with Adam's leaving. It would surely have been impossible for anyone to stay morose when surrounded by all these excited, giggling children, and frankly, seeing the problems some of the handicapped youngsters had to contend with had made her horribly ashamed of her own self-absorption.

'Makes you realise just how lucky you are, doesn't it?' Since Bernie, her agent, was apparently physically incapable of lowering his voice, his attempt at a murmur two inches away from her practically shattered her left eardrum. She turned to him with an affection-ate grin, knowing his soft heart had been hugely moved by the children that afternoon.

'Sure does. Is Ace ready to go on yet?'

Bernie's indiarubber face was as guileless as a child's. 'He says he won't go on without a warm-up act first.'

'He won't *what*?' She sent him a look of blank astonishment. 'But that wasn't part of the deal! In any case, there isn't a warm-up act here.'

'Oh yes, there is.' His kindly brown eyes narrowed shrewdly. 'A little birdie tells me you haven't been doing a great deal of singing recently. Well, this is just the time and the place—and the audience—for a comeback.'

'Has Candy put you up to this?' Rory demanded. 'So help me, I'll—I'll. . .'

'Thank her very much for being such a caring friend,' he finished for her. 'Come on, Rory—the kids would love to hear you sing. Don't let them down.'

Her eyes darted round the club as though seeking an escape route and she gave a hollow groan. 'Look, Bernie, I haven't been able to bring myself to tell you this, but I'm not sure if I'll ever be able to go back on stage. I've lost whatever it was that used to draw me there like a magnet.'

'You think I don't know that?' He aimed a softly affectionate punch at her arm. 'You don't stay in the business as long as I have without learning a little bit about people. And I reckon I know you pretty well.' He shrugged expressively. 'Hey, I'm not going to force you to do anything against your will—if you really have decided to quit the music business, then so be it. But for heaven's sake don't let fear drive you away from the stage. Now go on, get one of your most glittery frocks on and give those kids the performance of your life. Don't you think they deserve it?'

She could almost feel the internal battle raging within her, and for a long moment could do nothing but gaze at the stage, torn between seeing it as a hostile no-man's-land and home. But at last she gave a tiny nod.

'OK. But only for you.'

He shook his dark head. 'For yourself.'

Rory made her way woodenly to the dressing-room, shivering slightly as she heard the familiar sounds of the nightclub band tuning up. Moving slowly as though she could put off the dreaded moment forever, she changed into her favourite show costume—a long glittery number in gold. The kids would love it. She was just in the middle of doing her hair when she heard a light tap at the door, followed by the sound of Candy's voice.

'Are you decent? I've got a visitor here for you.'

For a moment she could barely breathe. A visitor? Could it possibly be. . .? The tiny darting flame of hope died instantly as the door swung open, but was replaced by a rush of real and genuine gladness as she looked into her father's face.

'Dad! Why didn't you let me know you were coming?' Caught between tears and laughter, she rushed into his arms, only now realising how much she'd missed his strength over the past few trying weeks.

'Easy, girl—you'll knock me over!' But even as he admonished her, he was hugging her close. 'I know what you've been going through,' he said gruffly. 'Candy's kept me in the picture.'

'Candy?' She looked at him in astonishment.

He nodded. 'Don't be mad at her, though, she was only doing as I'd asked. Remember I told you I'd be keeping tabs on you even though I was far away?'

'You did it through Candy.'

'Correct. And from what she tells me, it sounds as if you handled everything pretty well. Not at all sure I could have done it any better.'

Feeling closer to him than she had at any time since her mother's death, Rory hid her face against his shoulder. 'Thanks, Dad,' she whispered.

'Well, don't go getting eye make-up all over my good coat!' But he was smiling broadly as he held her away to arm's length. 'Look, sweetheart, you don't have to make up your mind one way or another right now— but the club's yours to run, if you want it.'

'What about you?' she queried.

'Me?' he chuckled richly. 'I've been leading the life of Riley since I got away from the place. Best thing I've ever done.' He tapped the side of his nose in an uncharacteristically arch little gesture. 'Between you and me and the gatepost, I've managed to get quite a few interesting little irons in the fire—projects I'd like to have time to work on.' He paused, eyeing her consideringly. 'But I don't want to pressure you. If you don't want the place, that's fine by me. I'll either bring someone else in to manage it, or sell it. It's up to you.'

Rory leaned against him, breathing in the familiar

smell of his aftershave, feeling strangely heady. It was
as though she'd been let loose from shackles she hadn't
even known she'd been wearing. Bernie and her father
had each, in their own way, released her from the
weight of obligation, setting her free to choose her own
path. If only someone could release her from the
shackles of loving Adam as easily, she thought ruefully.

'Thanks, Dad,' she murmured.

'Don't mention it,' he returned gruffly. 'Now, aren't
you supposed to be singing?'

She nodded. 'And that's all Candy's doing too.'

'Well, don't start till I get back into the audience,'
he commanded. 'I haven't heard you sing in ages.'

She watched him walk away along the corridor
heading back towards the club, her heart feeling lighter
than it had for the past week. Even the thought of
Candy acting as a spy in the camp couldn't annoy her—
she knew her friend well enough to be sure she would
have acted with Rory's best interests at heart.

As her opening music rang out, she ran up to the
wings, her spirits considerably buoyed up by knowing
her father was in the audience, and by the fact that
she'd felt a tiny but unmistakable buzz of excitement
on hearing those familiar chords. Bang on cue, she
strode out on to the stage, feeling none of the terror
that had crippled her last performance, the excited
cheers of the children bringing a beaming smile to her
face. For their sake she altered her normal style
considerably, emphasising the playful side of her personality, exhibiting none of her normal sultriness. Even
Adam would have seen the difference, she thought
wistfully. Then, as her eyes swept over the crowd
clustered round the stage, she did a double-take,

spotting one figure much larger and more powerful than the rest. It was him!

She never knew how she made it through to the end of the song. Having seen him, she found it impossible to drag her eyes away from him, and her pulse seemed to be racing at twice its normal rate, making a complete nonsense of her breathing control. A tiny voice of reason in her mind kept trying to convince her he was there only to bring her some new information about the court case, but her ridiculous heart refused to listen, all but taking wings within her as she sang. Finally she reached the last notes, and took a final bow, practically flinging the microphone at Candy, who had stepped on stage to act as compère.

'I suppose this was your doing too!'

Candy chuckled delightedly. 'Bringing Adam here, you mean? Not guilty, Your Honour. He came of his own free will.'

She turned away to announce Ace Elliott and Rory ran off stage, only to cannon straight into Adam standing in the wings. She began to apologise breathlessly, but his arms tightened about her.

'Were you by any chance in a hurry to get somewhere?' he asked mildly.

'Well, yes, I wanted to get to. . .' Flustered by his presence, thrown off balance by the feel of his hard body against her own, she suddenly clamped her mouth shut, horrified to realise she'd almost told him she'd been rushing to get to him. 'To get to the dressing-room,' she finished lamely.

'I hope that's a lie,' he returned gravely, 'since I broke all speed records getting from the dance floor to the wings.'

'You did?' She breathed incredulously. 'Why?'

Behind them Ace Elliot exploded on to the stage and Adam made a rueful grimace. 'Come on,' he mouthed, his words drowned out by the music. Grabbing her hand, he made his way back to the dressing-room, closing the door firmly behind them. Rory couldn't help but wonder if he could hear her heart beating, since it was thundering in her own ears like jungle drums.

'Now,' he said, 'in answer to your question—I hurried to the wings because I couldn't stand to let any more time than was strictly necessary go past without having you in my arms.'

'What?' Utterly astounded not only his words, but by the warm tenderness in his eyes, she glanced quickly round the room as if expecting to find watching eyes. 'Are we in the middle of another investigation?'

Adam chuckled richly and her eyes widened still more. Adam? Chuckling?

'No, we're not.' His expression sobered. 'You, Aurora Jennings Blake, have made me understand a little of what addicts must have to face when they're made to go cold turkey,' he said. 'This past week, being without you, has been sheer, unadulterated hell.'

'It has?' Sweet heaven, now her brain must have become addled, if that was the best she could come up with. 'Has it?' she added helpfully.

'I've spent the whole time trying to convince myself it could never work between us,' he went on, as though she hadn't spoken. 'We have nothing in common, and in temperament we're poles apart. We'll probably drive each other crazy.' He smiled ruefully. 'But the truth of the matter is, I need you, Rory. My life's nothing without you, my beautiful lioness.'

'Even though I'm just a brash and brassy singer?'

Suddenly flying as high as a kite, she couldn't resist the tiny gibe.

He pretended to wince. 'I deserved that! Look, Rory, I've been wrong about a lot of things in my life, but never more than I have been about you, right from the start. Because of Lisa, I created a picture of you in my mind. I decided you must be hard, self-seeking, ambitious to the point of ruthlessness, and immoral to boot.' He reached out one hand to stroke her cheek. 'Discovering that you were in reality generous, caring, sensitive and stunningly sexy was hard for me to cope with. Discovering how much I wanted you, right from the moment I saw you in the flesh for the first time, was harder still. So, to cover up the way I truly felt, I tried to alienate you.' He wound his fingers into her hair, using it to pull her gently towards him. 'That worked pretty well until that day in the forest.' He shook his head wonderingly. 'Then I discovered that on top of everything else I'd had wrong about you, you were a virgin. That really knocked all my cockeyed theories for six, and me with them!' He pressed his lips to her forehead. 'That's why I left you alone that evening, because I needed time to sort things out in my own mind.'

'Only to walk into an ambush!'

'Correct.' He held her away for a second, eyeing her curiously. 'By the way, I never did ask you—what made you come round to the cottage that night?'

Rory felt a warm blush creep up her cheeks. 'I was intending to ambush you too,' she confessed. 'Albeit in a somewhat different way. I wanted to know what the heck was going on between us!'

Adam laughed softly, deep in his throat. 'You and me both! Well, I know now, though it took some time before my stupid head would accept what my infinitely more sensible heart had been trying to tell it all along.'

'Which was what?' She was barely able to breathe as she looked up into his features, still strong but without that harsh granite edge she'd come to know so well.

'That I love you very deeply, Rory. Can you cope with that?'

She tilted her head to one side, pretending to consider the question. 'Cope with the love of a scorpion?' she said. 'I'm not sure. Candy's warned me that Scorpios are very possessive.'

'Very,' he growled, tightening his arms about her.

'Well, that's all right, since you're the only man I've ever wanted to be possessed by. I already know you're passionate. . .' She lifted her face for his kiss, groaning in soft satisfaction as his mouth claimed hers. Long moments later he lifted his head from hers, his eyes darker than ever as they gazed at her.

'Have you decided what you're going to do about the club?'

She nodded. 'I'm going to keep it, but put Candy in as manageress.'

'What about you?'

Her features grew serious. 'Thanks to what you told me about Lisa I now realise, perhaps for the first time, just how much influence people in the music world can have, albeit quite unknowingly, over impressionable youngsters. I'd like to organise an anti-drugs campaign.'

His hold on her tightened. 'Thank you,' he said softly. Then his mouth found hers again and the rest of the world could have disappeared without a trace without either of them being aware of it. Centuries later he lifted his head.

'They say it takes a brave woman to love a Scorpio,' he said.

Rory smiled. 'Then it's just as well I'm a Leo. Because what could be braver than a lion?'

STARGAZING

YOUR STAR SIGN: **SCORPIO (Oct 23–Nov 22)**

SCORPIO is ruled by the planets Mars and Pluto and controlled by the element of Water. These combinations tend to make you secretive and intense. Although others may be fooled by your easygoing nature, they will soon discover that you do not like to take advice and resent being told what to do!

Socially you prefer to be in the company of the people you know and trust, and it is only when a Scorpio is feeling relaxed that the glamorous side of their nature will be truly revealed.

Your characteristics in love: Scorpios are one of the signs that are governed by powerful emotions, making them intense and sensitive. And once you are involved with someone you pull out all the stops to show how passionate you can be! However, partners should be careful: when love is going well, Scorpios will invest all their energies—but if a relationship starts to go wrong, they are more than likely to display that famous sting in the tail!

186

Star signs which are compatible with you: Pisces, Cancer, Virgo and **Capricorn** are the most harmonious, while **Taurus**, **Leo** and **Aquarius** are a combination that will certainly not make for a dull relationship! Partners born under other signs can also be compatible, depending on which planets reside in their Houses of Romance and Personality.

What is your star-career? Scorpios enjoy positions in which they have plenty of power and influence, and you will always enjoy a job in which you can direct your passion and energy to the full. You are always good at coping with the unexpected and would have natural potential working in medicine, private detection or anything involving research.

Your colours and birthstones: You love bold, dramatic colours such as maroon which bring out the creative side to your sign. Indeed, the deep maroon and red shades of your gems beryl and red cornelian show the traditional link that many Scorpios are said to have with all that is mysterious and magical.

SCORPIO ASTRO-FACTFILE

Day of the week: Tuesday
Countries: Poland, Switzerland
Flowers: Rhododendron and any dark red flower
Food: Hot spices and rich creamy desserts; Scorpios can be very fussy about food and are often more likely to be the chef than the one who actually eats the food!
Health: Be careful not to let your emotions get the better of you! Scorpios are often likely to be over-sensitive to life's stresses and strains, although the Water element in your sign helps to cool and soothe you when things become too much!

You share your star sign with these famous names:

John Cleese   Jodie Foster
Yasmin Le Bon   Prince Charles
Lulu   Kim Wilde
Frank Bruno

Next Month's Romances

Each month you can choose from a wide variety of romance with Mills & Boon. Below are the new titles to look out for next month, why not ask either Mills & Boon Reader Service or your Newsagent to reserve you a copy of the titles you want to buy — just tick the titles you would like and either post to Reader Service or take it to any Newsagent and ask them to order your books.

Please save me the following titles:	Please tick	✓
RIDE THE STORM	Emma Darcy	
A DAUGHTER'S DILEMMA	Miranda Lee	
PRIVATE LIVES	Carole Mortimer	
THE WAYWARD WIFE	Sally Wentworth	
HAUNTING ALLIANCE	Catherine George	
RECKLESS CRUSADE	Patricia Wilson	
CRY WOLF	Amanda Carpenter	
LOVE IN TORMENT	Natalie Fox	
STRANGER PASSING BY	Lilian Peake	
PRINCE OF DARKNESS	Kate Proctor	
A BRIDE FOR THE TAKING	Sandra Marton	
JOY BRINGER	Lee Wilkinson	
A WOMAN'S LOVE	Grace Green	
DANGEROUS DOWRY	Catherine O'Connor	
WEB OF FATE	Helena Dawson	
A FAMILY AFFAIR	Charlotte Lamb	

If you would like to order these books in addition to your regular subscription from Mills & Boon Reader Service please send £1.70 per title to: Mills & Boon Reader Service, P.O. Box 236, Croydon, Surrey, CR9 3RU, quote your Subscriber No:.......................................
(If applicable) and complete the name and address details below. Alternatively, these books are available from many local Newsagents including W.H.Smith, J.Menzies, Martins and other paperback stockists from 6th November 1992.

Name:...

Address:..

....Post Code:.........................

To Retailer: If you would like to stock M&B books please contact your regular book/magazine wholesaler for details.

You may be mailed with offers from other reputable companies as a result of this application.
If you would rather not take advantage of these opportunities please tick box ☐

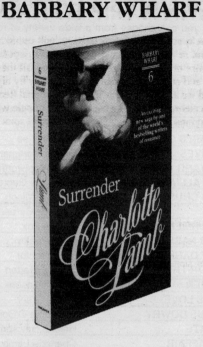

WIN A TRIP TO ITALY

Three lucky readers and their partners will spend a romantic weekend in Italy next May. You'll stay in a popular hotel in the centre of Rome, perfectly situated to visit the famous sites by day and enjoy the food and wine of Italy by night. During the weekend we are holding our first International Reader Party, an exciting celebratory event where you can mingle with Mills & Boon fans from all over Europe and meet some of our top authors.

HOW TO ENTER

We'd like to know just how wonderfully romantic your partner is, and how much Mills & Boon means to you.

Firstly, answer the questions below and then fill in our tie-breaker sentence:

1. Which is Rome's famous ancient ruin?

❑ The Parthenon   ❑ The Colosseum   ❑ The Sphinx

2. Who is the famous Italian opera singer?

❑ Nana Mouskouri   ❑ Julio Iglesias   ❑ Luciano Pavarotti

3. Which wine comes from Italy?

❑ Frascati   ❑ Liebfraumilch   ❑ Bordeaux

Tie-Breaker: Well just how romantic is your man? Does he buy you chocolates, send you flowers, take you to romantic candlelit restaurants? Send us a recent snapshot of the two of you (passport size is fine), together with a caption which tells us in no more than 15 words what makes your romantic man so special you'd like to visit Rome with him as the weekend guests of Mills & Boon.

....

....

....

....

Mills & Boon

In order to find out more about how much Mills & Boon means to you, we'd like you to answer the following questions:

1. How long have you been reading Mills & Boon books?

☐ One year or less   ☐ 2-5 years   ☐ 6-10 years

☐ 10 years or more

2. Which series do you usually read?

☐ Mills & Boon Romances   ☐ Medical Romances   ☐ Best Seller

☐ Temptation   ☐ Duet   ☐ Masquerade

3. How often do you read them?   ☐ 1 a month or less

☐ 2-4 a month   ☐ 5-10 a month   ☐ More than 10 a month

Please complete the details below and send your entry to: Mills & Boon Reader Service, FREEPOST, P.O. Box 236, Croydon, Surrey CR9 9EL, England.

Name: ....

Address: ....

.... Post Code: ....

Are you a Reader Service subscriber?

☐ No ☐ Yes my Subscriber No. is: ....

RULES & CONDITIONS OF ENTRY

1. Only one entry per household.
2. Applicants must be 18 years old or over.
3. Employees of Mills & Boon Ltd., its retailers, wholesalers, agencies or families thereof are not eligible to enter.
4. The competition prize is as stated. No cash alternative will be given.
5. Proof of posting will not be accepted as proof of receipt.
6. The closing date for entries is 31st December 1992.
7. The three entrants with correct answers who offer tie-breaker sentences considered to be the most appropriate and original will be judged the winners.
8. Winners will be notified by post by 31st January 1993.
9. The weekend trip to Rome and the Reader Party will take place in May 1993.
10. It is a requirement of the competition that the winners attend the Reader Party and agree to feature in any publicity exercises.
11. If you would like your snapshot returned, please enclose a SAE and we'll return it after the closing date.
12. To obtain a list of the winning entries, send a SAE to the competition address after 28th February, 1993.

You may be mailed with offers from other reputable companies as a result of this application. Please tick the box if you would prefer not to receive such offers. ☐